POWELL'S
Native
Animals
of New Zealand

4th edition

Edited by B.J. Gill

Curator of Land Vertebrates, Auckland Museum

Original text by A.W.B. Powell, updated by W.O. Cernohorsky,
B.J. Gill, A.B. Stephenson and K.A.J. Wise

David Bateman

Contents

Arthur William Baden Powell

1901-1987

A.W.B. Powell at work with shell specimens, Auckland Museum, c. 1960.

Photo: Auckland Star *(Auckland Museum Library collection).*

Baden Powell was born in Wellington and the family moved to Auckland when he was a baby. Powell went to Auckland Grammar School, and in his youth he developed a passion for conchology, the study of seashells. He worked as a commercial artist and lithographer from 1918 to 1929, when he was appointed conchologist at the Auckland Institute and Museum. He curated the mollusc collection at the museum for 39 years until his retirement in 1968, and also served as Assistant Director from 1936 until 1968. After retiring he continued at the museum as a research associate, and he kept on publishing books and articles until 1979.

During Powell's lifelong study of molluscs he described more than 1,000 new species or subspecies, and his technical papers were usually illustrated with his own exquisite drawings. His skill as an illustrator became widely admired after 1947 with the publication of Auckland Museum's handbook *Native Animals of New Zealand.*

Powell was elected a Fellow of the Royal Society of New Zealand in 1940. In 1956 the University of Auckland gave him an honorary D.Sc. degree. In the 1981 New Year's honours list Powell was awarded a C.B.E. for his contributions to marine science.

Foreword to the Fourth Edition

For several generations of New Zealanders interested in nature, A.W.B. Powell's *Native Animals of New Zealand* has been an introduction to the fauna of New Zealand, and a means of identifying common animals. The book's strengths are the simple descriptions, clear drawings and inexpensive format.

First published in 1947, *Native Animals* has remained in print ever since. The first print-run of 4,000 copies sold out within 14 weeks, and there were two reprintings. A second edition was published in 1951, and was reprinted five times, the last in 1975. The third edition appeared in 1987 and was reprinted in 1993. The first three editions sold a total of 147,000 copies, which surely makes it the biggest-selling nature book in the history of New Zealand publishing. *Native Animals* is still in demand despite competition from many other nature books, most of them lavishly illustrated in colour.

The original text was written by Powell with assistance with certain sections from E.G. Turbott and G. Uttley. For the 3rd edition (1987) the text was revised by several Auckland Museum staff: Walter Cernohorsky (molluscs and brachiopods), Brian Gill (vertebrates except fish and whales), Keith Wise (arthropods except crustaceans) and Brett Stephenson (all other groups). Our aim was to update the text and correct errors while retaining Powell's wording as much as possible. The original book was intended in part to be a guide to certain exhibits at Auckland Museum, and we removed references to particular specimens, many of which were no longer displayed.

The first two editions reproduced Powell's drawings in the format in which they were drawn, namely as half-page columns that suited letterpress printing. With the 3rd edition, offset printing allowed the illustrations to be released from their columns and rearranged so that text and respective figures were together on each double-page spread. A few new drawings by other artists were added to the 1987 edition.

Powell died on 1 July 1987, after the 3rd edition had gone to press. In this 4th edition, the title has been changed to *Powell's Native Animals of New Zealand* to link the originator more directly with his book. A biographical note about Powell has been added.

The 3rd edition species texts are reproduced here with editorial changes for improved consistency. I thank Wilma Blom, Jim Goulstone, Ramola Prasad and Fiona Thompson for checking Latin names and providing corrections.

In this edition a Māori name is provided for nearly every animal. These names were collated by Mr H.T. Rikihana, recently retired from Manukau Institute of Technology Te Whare Takiura o Manukau, to whom I am indebted. Only one Māori name is given for each animal (as with the English names), and where several are known we give the most commonly used.

The illustrations are unchanged from the 3rd edition but their arrangement has been improved. All are the work of A.W.B. Powell except for the following prepared for the 3rd edition: 215a, 252, 252a, 255, 256, 257 and 257a by Juliet Hawkins, and 317 and 318 by Brett Stephenson.

B.J. Gill
Curator of Land Vertebrates, Auckland Museum

Introduction

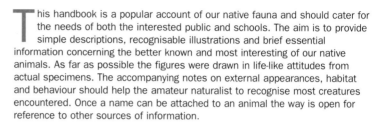

This handbook is a popular account of our native fauna and should cater for the needs of both the interested public and schools. The aim is to provide simple descriptions, recognisable illustrations and brief essential information concerning the better known and most interesting of our native animals. As far as possible the figures were drawn in life-like attitudes from actual specimens. The accompanying notes on external appearances, habitat and behaviour should help the amateur naturalist to recognise most creatures encountered. Once a name can be attached to an animal the way is open for reference to other sources of information.

In the following text, detailed classification and comparative anatomy have been largely omitted, for such information is readily obtainable in standard text books. However, the order in which the groups appear coincides approximately with their systematic position, and thus a sequence is maintained from the simplest of the invertebrates to the mammals. Since this handbook is concerned mainly with the sight identification of the animals, the protozoa and other groups that are mostly of microscopic size have been omitted.

Long isolation from other lands has allowed the New Zealand native fauna to develop largely free from outside influences. The fauna is not remarkably rich in species, and some widespread groups are either absent or poorly represented. Nevertheless, New Zealand has a wealth of endemic species with many peculiar developments and adaptations.

Except for one or two brief interludes, when land extensions to the north enabled certain Melanesian elements to enter, New Zealand has been separated from other lands since late Cretaceous times, about 85 million years ago. When mammals arose and spread over the larger land areas of the earth, New Zealand was already an island. Therefore, with the exception of three species of bats, the land remained free of mammals. The sea, however, was no barrier to the spread of aquatic species, and so what we lack in land mammals is compensated for by a considerable fauna of whales and seals.

The comparatively large number of our flightless birds is resultant upon the paucity of land mammals, for lack of competition and particularly immunity from attack by mammals, has enabled certain birds to become ground foragers, which habit has led to heavier build and reduced wings.

Our most remarkable flightless birds are the kiwis and the extinct moas – two extremes in size – the former little larger than a Domestic Fowl, and the latter up to 3 m high. Both are members of that group of southern hemisphere flightless birds to which belong the modern Ostrich, Emu and Cassowary. The presence of birds of this group can be explained only by the assumption that New Zealand was once a part of a great southern land mass.

The Tuatara gives distinction to the fauna, for it is the sole survivor of a group of reptiles which became extinct elsewhere at least 60 million years ago.

The land extensions to the north gave New Zealand the large *Placostylus* land snails, and in the flora, incidentally, the Kauri was a notable gain. Since New Zealand is one of the few considerable land masses contiguous to the great southern ocean, it is not surprising that many species of wide-ranging subantarctic sea birds come to this country during the breeding season.

On the other hand, warm-water marine organisms, particularly certain fish and shellfish, invade New Zealand seas, travelling south of their normal limits through the agency of a warm-water current which proceeds down the east Australian coast and thence across the Tasman to influence water temperatures as far south as the Auckland Islands. New Zealand is long and narrow, covering over 13 degrees of latitude, and this factor alone gives us a wide variety of marine organisms, many with a restricted range determined by water temperatures.

A thousand years of human settlement in New Zealand has upset the balance of primeval nature, causing immense changes in our native land fauna. Some species have failed to survive altered conditions, and others, once common, are now sadly reduced in numbers. In some areas almost all the characteristic native elements have been replaced by introduced creatures. Nevertheless, large tracts of native forest remain, and thus within range of most districts, one may still enjoy the splendour and solitude of primeval nature, and in so doing observe the creatures that are truly New Zealand.

Conditions of life in respect to the sea, however, have been less altered by the spread of commerce and the effects of the advance of cultivation on land. At the sea ports, harbour pollution has driven out a few species, but for the most part New Zealand coastal waters are still relatively clean. Of all the haunts of wildlife the seashore affords the greatest and most varied field for study. Animals and plants of infinite variety compete to maintain their existence in the narrow intertidal belt.

All life, vegetable and animal, revolves in a great cycle dependent in the first instance upon sunlight. This fact is apparent when marine organisms are studied. The sun's rays enable the plant forms (seaweeds and the microscopic diatoms) to manufacture their chemical food. Vegetarian organisms devour seaweeds; carnivorous species prey upon the vegetarian feeders; decaying vegetable and animal matter impregnates muds and accounts for a number of detritus feeders, which consume the mud and digest from it the organic particles; while planktonic feeders sift the minute drifting plant and animal organisms from the sea water. Finally, decaying plant and animal life enriches the sea, again to become available in chemical form to promote the growth of seaweeds and diatoms.

Sponges

New Zealand sponges are quite numerous and varied, but much more study is required before the fauna is adequately known. The dead sponge framework is a common object cast ashore on our beaches and encrusting species are frequently found living attached to the undersides of stones in the low tidal zone.

A sponge colony consists of vast numbers of individual animals contained in tiny cells of a fibrous skeletal framework. Through this framework larger tubular openings give access to ramifications which allow a free passage of water to bring food to the myriads of animals composing the colony. Water, laden with microscopic food, is induced to flow through the larger openings by the concerted rhythmic action of tiny hair-like processes with which each sponge animal is provided.

The living sponge bears little resemblance to the dried-out skeleton found on the beach. In life the sponge colony is heavy and is usually covered with a slimy coating, through which only the larger openings are visible to the eye. Most sponges have a skeleton of tangled horny fibres, but others are composed of spicules of calcium carbonate or silica. The spicules are generally microscopic, and present a great variety of beautiful and symmetrical forms in different species. Some are shaped like glassy needles, others like miners' picks, and a very common form is Y-shaped.

Old shells are frequently found that are so pitted with tiny holes that one would imagine that something akin to House Borer had been at work. This destruction is caused by a minute boring sponge, *Cliona*. Presumably its boring activities are in some way achieved by an acid secretion.

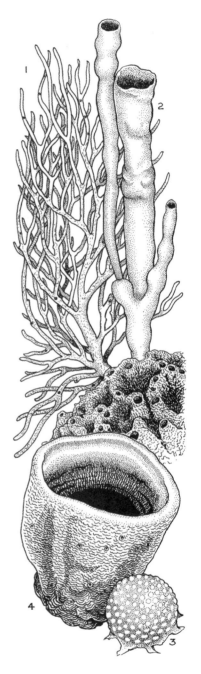

> The sponge is not, as you suppose,
> A funny kind of weed;
> He lives below the deep blue sea,
> An animal like you and me,
> Though not so good a breed.
> – A.P. Herbert

A general name for sponges in New Zealand is kōpūpūtai.

1. ### Long Finger Sponge (Kōpūpūtai Roa)
   Callyspongia ramosa
   Cast ashore very frequently on Auckland east coast beaches. Masses 600 mm long and over 300 mm wide are not uncommon. The skeletal mass is of light yellowish brown colour. The living colonies occur attached to rock below the lowest tidal level.

2. ### Organ Pipe Sponge (Pūngorungoru)
   Siphonochalina sp.
   Grows in the form of delicate thin-walled tubes up to 300 mm long and 25 mm or more in diameter. These tubes grow in erect position on the sea bed. The species was found originally in deep water off the coast of New South Wales.

3. ### Globe Sponge (Porotaka Moana)
   Tethya aurantium
   Brilliant orange and resembling a golf ball. It is common in the lower intertidal rocky zone attached to the undersides of boulders and to the roofs of caverns.

4. ### Large Cup Sponge (Kōpūpūtai Nui)
   Gellius imperialis
   This specimen was obtained in 75 m off Cape Brett. It is of bright red colour, and about 250 mm tall.

Coelenterates

Although of very diverse appearance, sea-anemones, the Mussel's-Beard, jelly-fish, sea-gooseberries, sea-pens and corals all belong to one group, the Coelenterata. These animals may occur as single individuals or polyps, like the sea-anemones, or they may form large colonies as in some corals and the Mussel's-Beard. The coelenterates have a single internal cavity, serving as a stomach, and a single opening above, which is encircled with tentacles and through which food enters and waste escapes. In the Common Jelly-fish the mouth is underneath and the umbrella is the equivalent of the body of a sea-anemone. Coral animals resemble sea-anemones, but have the ability of secreting a limy base, and the Mussel's-Beard is a vast colony of tiny anemone-like creatures which secrete an intricate branching framework of flexible horny material. A general name for coelenterates in New Zealand is poku kawekawe.

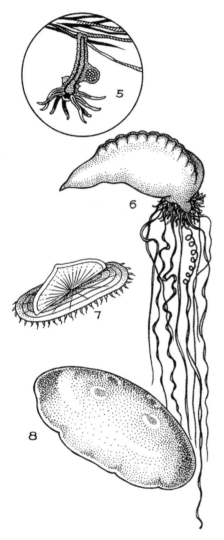

5. ### Freshwater Hydra *(Huru Moana)*
Hydra viridis
A solitary polyp about 10 mm long, usually found attached to the under surfaces of water plants in ponds and streams. This animal resembles a sea-anemone, but is even more simple in structure; just a hollow cylinder with a mouth surrounded by tentacles. *Hydra* catches its prey by means of these waving tentacles. There are two methods of reproduction – a lump of tissue appears at the side of the body, develops a mouth and tentacles and then breaks away as a new individual, or other swellings produce eggs and spermatozoa. Fertilisation takes place and embryo hydras develop independently. Several species of *Hydra* are known from New Zealand, but most are identical with European species. It is suspected that they are accidental importations since *Hydra* has been found only in the immediate vicinity of our larger cities.

6. ### Portuguese Man-of-war *(Ihu Moana)*
Physalia physalis
A colony of hydroid animals which combine to produce an air-filled bladder 25-150 mm long. This acts as a float and a sail to the large number of individual animals clustered beneath. Each animal is specialised in the performance of one of several duties. Some are feeders, some have no mouths but provide the stinging capsules, while others, like clusters of dark-blue grapes, bear the sexual cells. From the whole are suspended long tentacles which can inflict a sting, even upon humans, more powerful than that administered by nettle. The Portuguese Man-of-war is a beautiful peacock-blue. They inhabit oceanic surface waters, but are frequently cast ashore in large numbers. It is not uncommon to see hundreds of them left stranded at high-water line on Muriwai Beach, Auckland west coast.

7. ### By-the-wind Sailer *(Katiaho Rere)*
Velella velella
A smaller hydrozoan colony than the Portuguese Man-of-war, but resembles it in colour and organisation. Instead of the air-filled float it has an oblong membranous raft, set with a diagonal sail. The float is 30-45 mm long and the blue mass of polyps are crowded on the under side. It frequently comes ashore on our Auckland west coast beaches together with the Portuguese Man-of-war, the Violet Snail *(Janthina)* and the empty shells of the buoyant little Ram's Horn *(Spirula)*, the animal of which is related to the octopus. There is another hydrozoan colony of similar organisation known as *Porpita porpita*. It has a small circular disc for a float and is without a sail, but has the same bright peacock-blue colour. It has been found on several occasions cast ashore during winter months at Muriwai Beach.

8. **Common Jelly-fish** *(Petipeti)*
Aurelia aurita
This requires no introduction to Aucklanders, for in spring and summer it may be seen in countless thousands in the waters of Auckland Harbour and the Hauraki Gulf. *Aurelia* is an individual animal, not a colony as in the Portuguese Man-of-war and its kindred. The translucent umbrella of 75-125 mm across has four horseshoe-shaped lilac-coloured bodies showing through. These are the gonads or reproductive organs. The life history of *Aurelia* is complicated, for the fertilised egg develops into an oval-shaped embryo termed a planula, which sinks to the bottom of the sea. There it becomes attached at one end and bears a superficial resemblance to a hydra. After a time the body constricts just below the fringe of tentacles and ultimately becomes severed, the top portion swimming off as a perfect little jelly-fish. The process is repeated until a series of saucer-shaped discs is formed and liberated. There are many species of jelly-fish in New Zealand waters, but much work needs to be done before they are adequately known. From coastal ships, particularly in Cook Strait, a large brownish species *Cyanea capillata*, over 30 cm across, is frequently seen.

9. **Mussel's Beard** *(Kawekawe)*
Amphisbetia minima
A yellowish-brown, fine hair-like mass which grows commonly amongst low tidal seaweeds, in rock pools and especially upon the shells of living mussels. The colony is composed of tiny horny envelopes arranged symmetrically upon flexible filaments. Each normal envelope contains a hydroid animal, complete with its circlet of tentacles, and at intervals larger envelopes occur, the "gonotheca" or breeding cells (Fig. 9a). These larger envelopes develop tiny "medusae", like young jelly-fish, which are dispersed to form new colonies elsewhere. The hydroid colony increases by the simple process of budding and becomes distributed by the periodic generation and release of "medusae". There are numerous species of thecate hydroids in New Zealand waters. A common collective name for these creatures is the sea-firs. They are frequently mistaken for seaweeds.

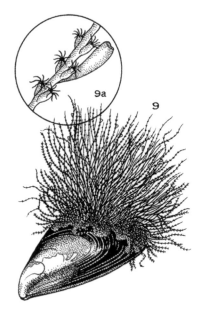

10. **Sea-gooseberry** *(Kanohi Moana)*
Pleurobrachia pileus
A free-swimming transparent animal resembling a jelly-fish, but with eight curious external bands of short comb-like structures which run from top to bottom of the oval or pear-shaped animal. These are used for propelling the creature through the water. From the lower or broad end there are two tendril-like threads, sometimes of considerable length. The body of the animal is 15-50 mm long. Very little has been written about New Zealand sea-gooseberries, but examples are commonly found by towing a muslin net from a small boat.

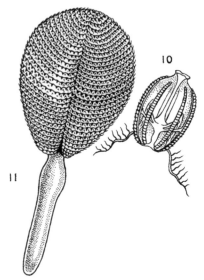

11. **Sea-pen** *(Mui Moana)*
Sarcophyllum bollonsi
A rare species, attaining a length of 150 mm, found at Doubtful Sound in 75 m. A second New Zealand species, *Virgularia gracillima*, has been dredged in Queen Charlotte Sound and at Lyttelton. The sea-pen is a colony of tiny anemone-like polyps arranged in a series on lateral branches of the upper part of a horny skeleton. The lower portion is narrowly cylindrical designed for embedding in the sea-bottom.

12. Red Sea Anemone (Kōtore Moana)
Actinia tenebrosa

One of our most abundant and widely distributed sea-anemones; easily recognised by its deep red or reddish-brown colour. When contracted it looks like a blob of red-currant jelly, but in an expanded condition there is a circle of numerous pink tentacles. It occurs on the shaded sides of rocks in the mid-tidal belt, and is a conspicuous object when found on the dark lava at Rangitoto Island. There are many species of New Zealand sea-anemones, often brilliantly coloured, but they are not easy to identify. The mouth of a sea-anemone is a fleshy opening in the centre of a circle of tentacles, and leads into the stomach which usually occupies about a third of the bulk of the body. Below the stomach there are a number of radially arranged cavities. Sea-anemones, in spite of their harmless, flower-like appearance, are voracious animals. They use the tentacles to ensnare and sting their victims before swallowing them whole. Indigestible parts are later disgorged. The food of sea-anemones consists of any small fish, shrimps and shellfish which come within range of the tentacles.

13. Wandering Sea-anemone (Hūmenga)
Phlyctenactis tuberculosa

Grows up to 200 mm long and is often found drifting among seaweeds at low tide. It is not permanently fixed to a base as are most anemones, but can attach or release itself at will. The surface is studded with bladder-like projections and it has numerous short tentacles encircling the open end. The colour of the outside is amber grey or light brown, and the tentacles are yellowish. The shape varies according to the mood of the animal – may be barrel-shaped when attached, or just a flabby collapsed cylinder when the creature is drifting. The species was found originally in Cook Strait, but in recent years it has been found on several occasions in Auckland waters.

14. Red Alcyonarian (Kotatea)
Alcyonium aurantiacum

A colony of tiny white polyps studded on a brilliant orange-red horny mass. The species was dredged originally by the French naturalists of the *Astrolabe* in 14-18 m in the Firth of Thames, Hauraki Gulf. It attaches to large shells and grows in masses up to 150 mm high. The tiny individual animals or polyps have narrow tentacles, always eight in number.

New Zealand waters are too cold for reef-building corals, but we have a number of species of true corals nevertheless. In structure the individual coral animal, or polyp as it is termed, is very like a sea-anemone, the chief difference being that the coral polyp has the ability to secrete a limy or chitinous base. A general name for corals in New Zealand is punga.

15. Cup Coral (Punga Moana)
Caryophillia profunda

A rare but widely distributed deep water species. These are simple corals, each cup representing the skeleton base of a single polyp.

16. Fan Coral (Pungatea)
Flabellum rubrum

Another simple coral about 40 mm in diameter found attached to rock and old shells at moderate depths in the Hauraki Gulf. The coral base is pure white and the animal scarlet. An intertidal relative, *Culicia rubeola*, is not uncommon, attached to the undersides of stones in North Auckland waters. The coral base is dull brownish and the animal salmon to dull vermilion.

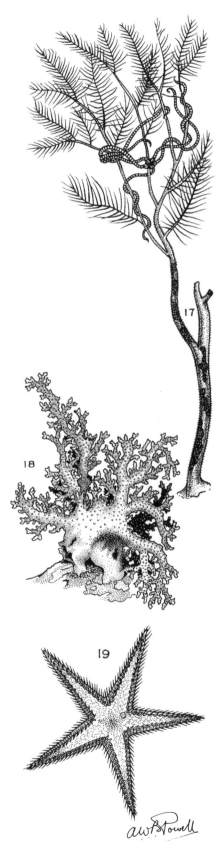

17. **Sea-tree** *(Tōtara)*
Aphanipathes sp.
Known technically as an antipatharian coral, it looks very like a gnarled shrub. It is attached by a root-like base to the sea-bottom and grows about 1.5-2 m high with branches 10-50 mm thick. The polyps are minute and are arranged on the feather-like portions. The branches and stem are the supporting skeleton which is formed of hard flexible chitin, having the appearance of ebony. The Sea-tree is very strong and many fishermen's nets have been torn to pieces by fouling these obstructions. Large brittle-stars with ringed legs, in purple and white, are found entwined amongst the branches of this coral, for they feed on the individual polyps. One of these brittle-stars is shown in the illustration. The Sea-tree is found in 75-180 m on rocky ground. It is abundant off Cape Brett and the Three Kings Islands.

18. **Red Coral** *(Punga Kura)*
Errina sp.
Occurs abundantly in deep water off the coast of Stewart Island and the Chatham Islands. It is not a true coral, but a member of a specialised group which can be likened to calcified sea-firs. They are almost invariably elegantly branched and of pink or red colour. In New Zealand, clumps of *Errina* up to 300 mm or more in diameter have been obtained.

Echinoderms

Starfish and sea-urchins are a well-known group to which belong also the bêche-de-mer sea-slugs and the sea-lilies (crinoids). They are known collectively as the Echinodermata, which means "spiny-skinned". The echinoderms are an early offshoot from the main lines of evolution. They are complex organisms so utterly different from other groups that comparison is difficult.

The spiny skin differs in development in the several kinds of creatures classed as echinoderms. Thus a starfish has a network of calcareous spiny plates embedded in tissue and muscle, but in a sea-urchin the plates are fused into a mosaic resulting in a rigid shell, while in the holothurians or bêche-de-mer sea-slugs the plates are sparse and embedded in the skin.

The most distinctive structure of the echinoderms is an elaborate water pumping system which operates numerous feeler-like processes known as tube-feet. These tube-feet are very noticeable in the under side of a starfish, and they assist greatly in the locomotion of the animal.

An echinoderm has no head, and so in the case of a starfish the initiative automatically shifts to the arm which happens to be in the creature's intended direction of movement. Then the other arms operate in perfect coordination with the leading member.

A general name for echinoderms in New Zealand is kiri taratara.

19. **Comb Star** *(Pekapeka)*
Astropecten polyacanthus
A perfect five-pointer 200-250 mm across, of buff or yellowish brown colour, very spiny at the sides and underneath, but with a dense pile-like texture on top. It is found on sandy bottoms from low-water to about 55 m. Occasionally it is found on sandy flats between tides in coastal localities. Distributed around the North Island east coast and southern Australia.

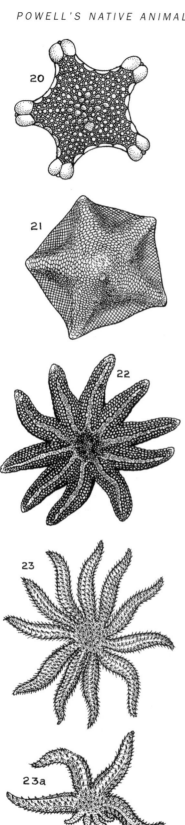

20. Biscuit Star (Kapu Ringa)
Pentagonaster pulchellus

Shaped and coloured like a fancy biscuit. The pairs of rounded knobs at each extremity have a slightly browned appearance just like a well-cooked biscuit. It attains a diameter of about 75 mm and is fairly common cast ashore on the South Island sandy beaches. It has not been recorded in the North Island north of Napier.

Fire Brick (Kapu Ura)
Asterodiscus truncatus

A large and brilliantly coloured species taken occasionally by trawlers operating in the vicinity of the Hen and Chicken Islands and in the Bay of Plenty. It is more plentiful, however, in deep water off the coast of New South Wales, where the local fishermen call it the Fire Brick on account of its flaming colours. The coloration is magnificent; chrome, heavily blotched with vermilion, the larger tubercles and the terminal plates being mauve to purple. It resembles *Pentagonaster* in shape, but is much larger and relatively thicker. One is reminded of a confection heavily sprinkled with "hundreds and thousands". (Not figured.)

21. Common Cushion Star (Kapu Parahua)
Patiriella regularis

Common almost everywhere between tide marks from North Cape to Stewart Island. It is more truly of pentagonal shape than *Pentagonaster*. Greyish-green and dark blue-green are the usual colours, but it is sometimes yellow, dull orange or even purple. It grows up to 100 mm across and is found near rocks on sandy or muddy tidal flats.

Inflated Cushion Star (Kapu Parahua Rahi)
Stegnaster inflatus

A rare species, similar to the Common Cushion Star in outline, but larger, much thicker, arched in the middle and usually more brilliantly coloured. The colouring may be buff, orange, orange-vermilion, purple or greyish-green. Both cushion stars are actively carnivorous and, like most starfish, have the habit of extruding the stomach and predigesting their victim before it is actually swallowed. Starfish exert great muscular power in forcing open bivalve shells upon which they frequently feed. The range of *Stegnaster* is Hauraki Gulf to Timaru. The only locality where it is at all common is the Takapuna coast, Auckland, at extreme low tide on rocky ground. (Not figured.)

22. Sun Star (Pātangaroa)
Stichaster australis

This is the large ungainly species common on surf-beaten rocks from North Cape to Milford Sound. The arms, which are shorter than the diameter of the central disc, vary in number between 10 to 13. It is grey, tinged with blue and orange. On the Auckland west coast these stars grow to about 250 mm across and are commonly seen feeding on mussel beds.

23. Spiny Star (Papatangaroa)
Coscinasterias calamaria

Our most abundant starfish, easily recognised by its rather slender prickly arms, which are longer than the width of the central disc. It is drab-coloured and sometimes reaches a diameter of 350 mm. Frequently, examples are seen which have suffered injury and are in the process of growing new arms (Fig. 23a).

Giant Seven-armed Starfish (Tangaroa Wae Whitu)
Astrostole scabra

Our largest starfish. Similar to *Coscinasterias* but has only seven arms. It grows up to 750 mm across and is known from Mahia Peninsula to Akaroa. (Not figured.)

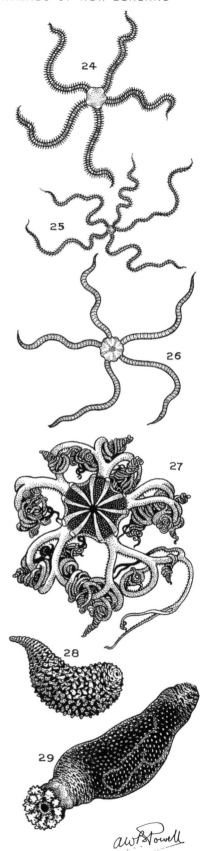

24. Common Brittle-star *(Weki Huna)*
Ophionereis fasciata

About 100-120 mm in diameter. A protectively coloured greyish speckled creature, living under stones that rest on sand and gravel. All the brittle-stars differ from ordinary starfish in having slender arms, used solely for locomotion. The organs of the body are all crowded into the small rounded central disc. Brittle-stars are fairly active and will cast off limbs readily, to avoid capture.

25. Rose-coloured Brittle-star *(Weki Riki)*
Amphiura rosea

A small, pink, very slender-armed species which is abundant in soft mud in from 10-35 m in the Hauraki Gulf. It lives in company with the Heart Urchin and the thin-shelled bivalve *Dosinia lambata*. This trio has adapted to a substratum which is unfavourable for most forms of life. Several species of *Amphiura* are known in New Zealand. A few of them live under stones between tide marks, but most occur in deep water.

26. Snake Tail *(Weki)*
Pectinura maculata

A large reddish-brown brittle star with five smooth, rounded, jointed arms, each suddenly tapered towards the tip. They sometimes grow over 300 mm across. Found among seaweed from low-tide to about 20 m throughout New Zealand, but rather uncommon.

27. Medusa-head Starfish *(Pekapeka Rau)*
Gorgonocephalus novaezelandiae

An endemic deep water species (200-500 m) often found living on the Black Tree-coral. An allied deep-water English species is better known and derives its popular name from the many branched arms like the tangle of snakes about the head of a Gorgon. The Medusa-head Starfish uses some of its many branched arms to fasten itself tendril-like to deep sea growth while the free arms are used for gathering food.

28. Sea Cucumbers *(Rori)*
29.

These belong to the same group as the tropical pacific Bêche-de-mer which has long been fished commercially and shipped to China as a food delicacy. Our common species (*Stichopus mollis:* not figured) is a mottled, light brown and white, warty, sausage-shaped "slug" 100-150 mm long, found on low tidal rocks and in rock pools throughout New Zealand. When expanded the sea cucumber has a circle of tentacles at one end surrounding the mouth. Although soft-bodied, the skin is tough and leathery, with embedded curious hard plates shaped like tiny wheels and anchors. The sea cucumber may be likened to a soft-bodied sea-urchin, drawn out from mouth to vent into a sausage-shaped body. Figures 28 and 29 show two deep-water species. The first lives in soft mud at about 30 m in Queen Charlotte Sound. The second was taken in 23 m at Paterson Inlet, Stewart Island.

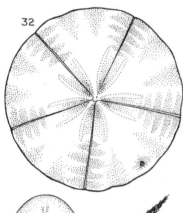

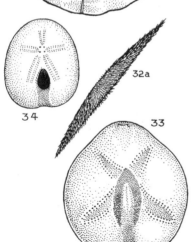

30. Tailed Sea Cucumber (Rori Whiore)
Caudina coriacea

This is 80-120 mm long, and is easily recognised by the tapering of one end like a rat's tail. It lives buried in mud with only the "tail" projecting, to maintain a respiratory current of water. It occurs at moderate depths in the Hauraki Gulf and at Bluff. Occasionally they are cast ashore in large numbers at New Brighton, near Christchurch.

31. Sea Lily (Rau Wheke)
Comanthus novaezelandiae

Obtained originally from 120 m off the Three Kings Islands; three species of crinoids (sea lilies) are known from New Zealand but they are all fairly rare. Living crinoids are survivors of very ancient stock, and they were much more abundant in earlier geological ages. Crinoids are like starfish with branched arms, but they are usually fixed either temporarily or permanently to some solid object. The New Zealand members are of the temporarily fixed group for they have a circle of cirri or small tentacles which are used to anchor the animal to the branching tree-like deep-water antipatharian coral upon which they are usually found.

32. Cake Urchin (Kina Papa)
Fellaster zelandiae

Common in fine sand of even texture, but only in certain locations, just within the entrance to large harbours, where there is high salinity but comparative shelter. They occur from low water to a few metres depth and are especially abundant at Pilot Bay, Tauranga Harbour, and on the shallow water sand banks of the outer portion of the Manukau Harbour. Fishermen of the Manukau call this urchin the "Snapper Biscuit", since the Snapper feeds upon the half-grown examples to some extent. The Cake Urchin is a hard limy disc from 75-100 mm in diameter, flat on the lower side, and slightly convex above, covered in life with short mossy-green spines. The shell, or "test" as it is termed in the echinoderms, is composed of a mosaic of pieces as in the Common Sea Urchin, and it readily breaks into five approximately triangular segments. These segments show the internal strengthening structure of props and pillars. It is extraordinary what little space is available for the animal. The animal feeds by swallowing quantities of sand from which it extracts organic detritus. The second illustration (Fig. 32a) shows this urchin in profile and emphasizes its flatness.

33. Heart Urchin (Kina Pākira)
Echinocardium australe

Abundant around the coasts of the main islands of New Zealand. It lives buried in soft mud from extreme low tide down to about 30 m. The test is extremely thin and fragile, 20-40 mm long, and is covered with fine curved glistening greenish-grey spines. When the tests of these urchins wash ashore they are usually denuded of spines as in the illustration. Large areas of the sea-bottom in the Hauraki Gulf are populated with an animal community consisting of *Echinocardium*, the brittle-star *Amphiura rosea*, and the bivalve shellfish *Dosinia lambata*.

34. Kina Poka
Echinobrissus recens

Resembles the Heart Urchin, but is smaller, more flattened, and much stronger. It differs notably from the Heart Urchin by the presence of an oval opening, eccentrically placed, in a shallow groove on the upper surface. The New Zealand species is not common, but is cast ashore at times on beaches at Nelson and Stewart Island. It belongs to a group that has survived with little change from the Jurassic period of 140 million years ago.

35. Kina Taratara
Goniocidaris umbraculum
A deep-water species found in Cook Strait, Foveaux Strait and off Otago Heads. It is notable for disparity in the form of its spines; some are pointed, others club shaped, a few have incipient branches and some terminate in flat or concave rounded discs.

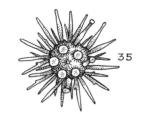

35

36. Common Sea Urchin (Kina)
Evechinus chloroticus
Found towards low tide in rock pools and crevices amongst seaweeds. It grows 100-200 mm in diameter and in life is conspicuous with its dense covering of long dark greenish spines. When the spines are removed there is a depressed circular limy "shell" of light greenish colour, composed of a mosaic of plates, many of which have small rounded knobs, arranged in regular series. These are the bosses upon which the movable spines are attached. Between the rows of bosses there are perforated plates through which the soft tube-feet operate and these are connected with an internal water pumping system characteristic of all urchins and starfish. The sea urchin moves about by the concerted action of the long spines and the tube feet. The large circular opening underneath is the mouth, largely occupied by a five-sided bony structure, the jaws, and referred to as Aristotle's lantern, for it bears a striking resemblance to an ancient lantern. The animal of a sea urchin is very fluid except for five bodies, like segments of an orange, both in shape and colour. These are the genital glands, which in the breeding season become enormously swollen with eggs. Many people, the Māori in particular, eat the sea urchin animal in a raw state.

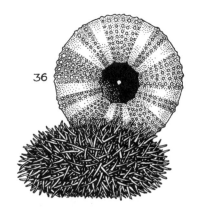

36

Annelid Worms

These are the true worms, which have their long narrow bodies divided by rings into numerous segments. Earthworms progress by alternately extending and contracting their bodies, at the same time obtaining a purchase by means of inconspicuous bristles on their sides. Their marine relatives, the polychaetes, differ in having these bristles much enlarged and so conspicuous that they resemble legs. Earthworms are mainly vegetable feeders dragging decayed leaves and twigs into their burrows and partially devouring them. While burrowing, worms swallow quantities of earth absorbing any organic matter contained in it, but bringing the greater part to the surface as "worm-casts". Charles Darwin described how worms on an acre of pasture were capable, in a year, of bringing ten tons of new earth to the surface in this way. The earthworm therefore is a valuable agent in the enrichment of the soil.

There is a considerable number of native species of earthworms in New Zealand, but few of them occur in land under cultivation. In the gardens and fields they have been largely replaced by accidentally introduced kinds. A giant worm from Little Barrier Island *(Diporochaeta gigantea)* attains a length of 1.3 m and a diameter of over 10 mm.

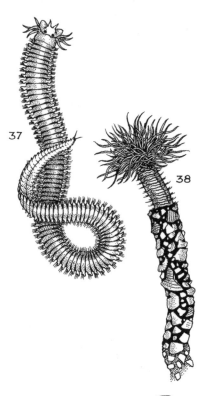

37

38

37. Sea Centipede (Weri Moana)
Perinereis novaehollandiae
Grows to 205 mm or more long and is a common species under stones at low tide. This and a large number of marine worms are the polychaetes ("many bristles"), so named because of the conspicuous bunches of bristles which operate like legs.

38. Mason Worm (Toke Waitai)
Thelepus spectabilis
Forms a protective tunnel or case to which fragments of shell and sand are attached. It is found partly buried in shell-sand and under stones and in rock pools at low tide.

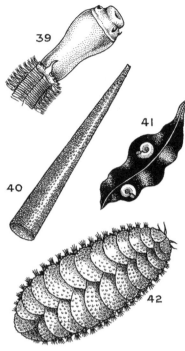

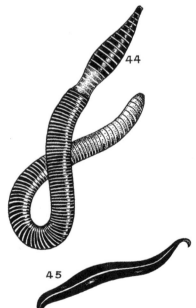

39. Thorny Worm *(Toke Moana)*
Glycera americana
A large slender species found in mud at low water. It sometimes grows to nearly 600 mm long. Only the curious head is shown, which bears four short curved hooks resembling thorns.

40. Sand-tube Worm *(Piri Torino)*
Pectinaria australis
Forms a graceful very fragile, tapered tube, about 50 mm long, and made up of agglutinated grains of sand. The tube, which resembles the shell of the mollusc *Dentalium*, is often washed ashore particularly on sheltered beaches, in harbours.

41. Spiral Worm *(Piri Ngongo)*
Paralaeospira sp.
Makes a tiny flattened spiral shell which is found attached to seaweeds. They may be found on almost any bunch of brown seaweed cast ashore on our beaches.

42. Sea Mouse *(Kutukutu)*
Lepidonotus polychroma
A broadly oval worm with two series of overlapping plates or scales down the back and numerous pairs of tufted bristles extending sideways from the under surface of the body. It is of dull brownish colour, about 75 mm long, and is found half buried in mud or under stones at low tide, but only in the southern parts of New Zealand.

43. Spiny Tubeworm *(Toke Pā)*
Pomatoceros caeruleus
Forms coral-like masses up to 900 mm in diameter and more than 300 mm high. The strong shelly individual tubes are irregular, prominently ridged and with a spiny projection overhanging the round aperture. The worms are 20-30 mm long and occupy only the outer end of their tubes, the middle of the colony consisting of old tubes and compacted mud. This worm may be found as isolated tubes cemented to intertidal rocks as well as in colonies as described above.

44. Zebra Earthworm *(Toke Moana)*
Notoscolex equestris
Found burrowing in leaf mould at the Poor Knights Islands, off the east coast of North Auckland. It is just over 200 mm long and is our only earthworm that could be considered handsome. The body is banded, zebra-fashion, with broad alternate zones of pale cream and purplish-brown.

Other Worms

45. Land Flatworms *(Toke)*
Geoplana spp.
Also called planarians, these are very flat, narrowly leaf-shaped, slug-like animals, which are found in damp places under logs and stones. There are over twenty native species and they reach 50-200 mm long. They are usually dull brownish and very slimy, but the figured specimen, taken at Waiheke Island, is black with a narrow white stripe down the middle. Planarians are carnivorous, feeding largely on earthworms. Allied to the planarians are a number of parasitic worms like the liverfluke which infests sheep, and the tapeworm which may occur in the intestines of man. All these worms have flat bilaterally symmetrical bodies, without the segments of true worms.

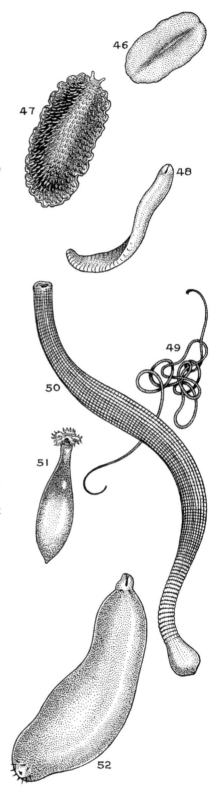

46. **Brown Marine Flatworm** *(Toke Piri)*
Leptoplana brunnea
A small oval creature 20-50 mm long, common under stones at low tide in Auckland waters. It has no distinct head or tentacles, and is brownish, darkest at the middle, and minutely speckled all over in dark brown.

47. **Frilled Marine Flatworm** *(Toke Papa)*
Thysanozoon brocchii
Occurs in the same location as the previous species. It differs in having the whole of the back covered with short tentacle-like processes as well as a beautifully waved or undulating margin. When this creature swims the margin or edges of the animal are rapidly undulated, reminiscent of the graceful actions of a ballet dancer. It grows to 50 mm long and is pale grey marbled with white and reddish-brown. Both species resemble the nudibranch sea-slugs, but these are molluscs having gills and rhinophores, those curious club-like organs near the front of the body.

48. **Nemertine Worm** *(Toke Waitai)*
Cerebratulus sp.
A common intertidal worm of a dull orange colour. It is flat in cross-section. Nemertine or proboscis worms are bottom dwellers living in shallow water under stones, in seaweed, or in sand and mud.

49. **Gordian Worm** *(Toke Rirapa)*
Gordius sp.
A thread-like worm of 150-200 mm long which coils itself into a tangle, hence the reference to the classical "Gordian-knot". This is the hair-worm of ponds, streams, and ditches. Many country folk in England have a fanciful notion that this worm is generated from horsehairs that have fallen in the water. The larvae of these worms are parasitic in the bodies of aquatic insects.

50. **Long Siphon Worm** *(Toke Whārōrō)*
Sipunculus maoricus
Belongs to a group of worms that are segmented in their early stage, but show no trace of this feature in the adult. They are of various shapes – some long and worm-like – others swollen like a sausage. They possess the curious ability of turning the front of their bodies outside-in so that the head disappears inside the body. They feed by swallowing quantities of sand or mud from which they extract organic particles. This worm is about 200 mm long and white with grooves running both ways which cut the surface into tiny squares.

51. **Flask-shaped Siphon Worm** *(Toke Hue)*
Dendrostoma aeneum
This is about 200 mm long, and shaped like an old-fashioned soda water bottle. It is a dirty-brownish colour and groups of them are often found under stones resting on mud in the low tidal zone. At the narrow end there is a frilled tentacular fold surrounding the mouth. The figured species occurs in the North Island, but in the South Island there is a similar species *Physcosoma annulatum*.

52. **Sausage Worm** *(Toke Mōmona)*
Echiurus novaezelandiae
A smooth inflated worm 120-200 mm long which lies buried in soft mud from shallow water to a few metres. It varies from dull salmon colour to bright purplish red. At the front end there is a short proboscis with a slit down one side. Behind this there are two metallic-looking hooks, like rose thorns, and a ring of similar processes at the posterior end. The species was described from material cast ashore at New Brighton, near Christchurch.

Brachiopods (Lamp-shells)

Although they resemble sea-shells the so-called lamp-shells are not molluscs, but a distinct group of very ancient lineage, really more akin to the Bryozoa. The name lamp-shell is derived from the fact that in typical forms the bivalved shell, more or less oval in form, shows a round hole at one end through which the animal attaches itself to rock or some other solid object. The shell therefore bears a striking resemblance to an ancient Roman lamp which was a closed-in oval dish with an opening at one end for the wick. The shelly valves of a brachiopod are not left and right as in a true shellfish, but upper and lower. To the inside of the lower valve are fastened delicate shelly loops which support the brachia, fleshy arms which combine the functions of breathing and directing small food particles to the mouth. A peculiar feature of the inside of a brachiopod is the relatively small size of the soft parts.

In the distant Palaeozoic era brachiopods were dominant animals of the sea, but they have gradually dwindled and now there are relatively few living species. There are nine species of brachiopods living in the New Zealand region. The Māori name for brachiopods is taurite papa moana.

53. Large Red Brachiopod (Papa Kura)
Magasella sanguinea
This has a radially ridged shell of bright red colour, up to 40 mm in diameter. It occurs in shallow to moderately deep water from Cook Strait southwards, being most plentiful at Stewart Island, where it frequently washes ashore. It is found on muddy or sandy bottom, usually attached to shells. There is a related species common on Horse Mussel shells (*Atrina*), in 25-35 m in the Hauraki Gulf. This is *M. haurakiensis*.

54. Small Red Brachiopod (Papa Kura Iti)
Waltonia inconspicua
Grows 10-20 mm in diameter, and is smooth and deep red in colour when not encrusted. It is found throughout New Zealand, but only in a few localities does it occur commonly in the intertidal zone. At Rangitoto Island, for instance, immense numbers crowd the under surface of the lava blocks at low tide, but elsewhere in the Auckland district the species is scarcely ever found. Other localities where it occurs commonly are Stewart Island and the Chathams.

55. Black Brachiopod (Papa Pōuri)
Notosaria nigricans
A broadly oval, radially ribbed, purplish black brachiopod up to 20 mm in diameter, strongly flexed and of variable outline. It is most commonly seen at Stewart Island and the Chatham Islands.

56. Large Oval Brachiopod (Papa Nui)
Neothyris lenticularis
Our largest species, with a smooth inflated shell over 50 mm in diameter, characterised by an extremely small foramen or opening. The colouring ranges from dull pink to an ashy-grey. The species is of southern distribution and occurs commonly on the oyster beds in 18-27 m in Foveaux Strait. Fig. 56a shows the form of the shelly loop in *lenticularis*, and Fig. 56b illustrates a vertical section through a typical brachiopod. The brachia attached to the loop and the muscles for operating the upper valve of the shell are shown.

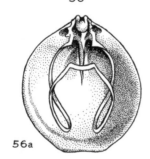

Bryozoans

The name Bryozoa means "moss-animals". These are the "sea-mats"; colonies of tiny animals with either a horny or limy covering which form coral-like growths or else encrust the surfaces of seaweeds, shells and stones. They occur in salt and fresh waters, but mostly in the former. Although some species resemble corals the Bryozoa are much more complex. Some grow as broad flexible fronds, or as miniature trees; others spread as a delicate tracery around the stems and fronds of seaweeds. The most beautiful forms are the so-called "lace-corals", bright pink or cream rosettes of open-textured calcium carbonate.

A number of bryozoans possess peculiar external accessory organs of uncertain function known as "avicularia" and "vibracula". The former resemble the head of a bird, and in life the jaws are constantly opening and shutting, seizing and holding small organisms or particles which come within range. The "vibracula", as the name suggests, are constantly in motion. Both these organs probably function in feeding, and in keeping the colony free from the deposition of sediment. The body of a bryozoan within its hard casing is shaped like a letter "U"; the first stroke of the "U" being a compensating sac and the second or up-stroke the body proper which is crowned with tentacles. The compensating sac takes in water which forces the body upwards and the tentacles out of the opening into a feeding position. For such small creatures the bryozoa are very complex in structure.

A large number of bryozoans have been described, but a specialist's knowledge is essential for the recognition of most of the New Zealand species. The Māori name is takapau moana.

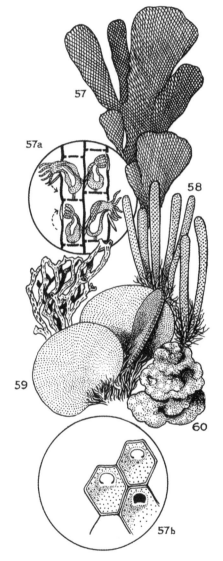

57. Sea-mat (Punga Rimurapa)
Beania pulchella
This is not hard and limy, but composed of a brownish flexible material. It is very like a seaweed in appearance, but a glance with a lens shows that both surfaces are composed of a fine network of regular cells arranged back to back, a single layer opening on each side. The figured example is from Cape Maria van Diemen. Fig. 57a shows how a typical bryozoan is extended into a feeding position by the operation of the compensating sac, as described above. Fig. 57b shows the outward appearance of bryozoans of the encrusting type. They grow together in close formation and form regular geometric patterns.

58. Steginoporella neozelanica
It grows in clusters of curved cylindrical hard limy rods, about 50 mm long, each with a honeycombed surface, the cavities being occupied by the individual animals. Each rod is anchored by a series of threads. It is found washed ashore at Cape Maria van Diemen and on other northern beaches.

59. Steginoporella perplexa
Similar to the above in detail, but the colonies assume the form of thin spreading white discs instead of cylindrical brownish rods. Found at Cape Maria van Diemen also.

60. Celleporaria agglutinans
This forms the massive free lumps resembling weathered pumice, which frequently wash ashore on harbour beaches. The surface is greyish to white, irregular, with slightly raised pimply protuberances, and the whole is minutely pitted, the pits being the vacant cells.

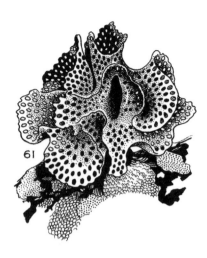

61. *Lace-coral* (*Punga Tatari*)
Hippellozoon novaezelandiae
A very beautiful bryozoan colony of distinctive form, for it is always like a delicately folded rosette of lace. The thin layers are hard and limy, perforated with numerous regular holes, and the cell openings are on the upper surfaces only. The figured example is orange colour and comes from 75 m off Cape Brett. Other New Zealand species, mostly from deep water, form colonies of several centimetres in diameter and are white, cream or red. Remains of a pink species form much of the sea bed in 160-275 m off the Three Kings Islands.

Molluscs (Shellfish)

The first difficulty encountered with shellfish is in the name, for not all "shellfish" possess shells, and a large number of the known species dwell exclusively on dry land. The difficulty is overcome by the use of the scientific term "mollusc", which means "soft-bodied". They may or may not possess an external or an internal shell. The animal is not jointed as in the worms and crustaceans, and each mollusc is one complete unit. It may surprise those who have not studied shellfish to learn that the octopus and the garden slugs are molluscs just the same as oysters, whelks, limpets and snails. A general name for shellfish in New Zealand is kiko ngohengohe.

The phylum Mollusca is divided into seven classes:

The Univalves (Gastropoda).
Periwinkles, limpets, whelks, snails etc. The shell is in one piece, usually spirally coiled. They live in the sea, on land and in fresh water. The garden slug is a land univalve that no longer secretes a shell.

The Tusk Shells (Scaphopoda).
Rather uncommon deep-water shellfish contained in small tapering tubes open at both ends. They live only in the sea.

The Solenogasters (Aplacophora).
Usually very small, worm-like molluscs which are covered with calcareous spicules. They live at great depth in the sea and feed on bottom-dwelling animals or organic debris.

The Chitons (Polyplacophora).
Limpet-like creatures composed of eight movable shelly valves surrounded by a leathery girdle. They are exclusively marine.

The Gastroverms (Monoplacophora).
Small, thin, limpet-like cap-shaped molluscs with five or six pairs of muscle scars. Animal with five or six pairs of gills and a radula. Termed "living fossils", they are survivors of a group of marine molluscs believed to have become extinct about 300 million years ago. Discovered in 1952, only about 10 species are known all of which live at great depth. Absent from New Zealand.

The Bivalves (Bivalvia).
Cockles, mussels, oysters and all shells composed of two pieces or valves hinged together with a flexible ligament. They live in the sea and in fresh water.

The octopus and its allies (Cephalopoda).
The highest developed of all the shellfish. They have long sucker-bearing "arms", really legs, since they have been derived from the foot of the animal. The octopus no longer grows a shell, but it is a near relative to the beautiful white-shelled Paper Nautilus. They are exclusively marine.

Bivalves

The Māori name for bivalves is papa moana rua.

62. Razor Mussel (Kute)
Solemya parkinsoni

A thin-shelled bivalve about 50 mm long covered with a dark chestnut-coloured shining epidermis which extends beyond the edge of the shell as a scalloped fringe. The live *Solemya* lives deeply buried in soft mud, but the dead shells wash ashore on beaches. They may be found by digging at low tide at St. Helier's Bay, Auckland, and in Tauranga Harbour.

63. Large Dog Cockle (Kuhakuha)
Tucetona laticostata

Lives half buried in sand and shelly beds in waters 5-30 m deep. It grows to about 80 mm in diameter, is very thick, strengthened on the outside by radial ridges. The hinge-teeth are of a primitive style, simple interlocking short ridges and pits, occupying most of the upper margin of the shell. The colouring is light reddish brown, blotched and mottled on a whitish ground. The ribs bear interrupted markings of dark reddish-brown. The species is common in both the North and South Islands and at the Chathams. Beds of them occur in Auckland waters in the Rangitoto and Motuihe Channels and they are frequently cast ashore on Takapuna Beach.

64. Golden Oyster (Poro)
Anomia trigonopsis

This is not a true oyster. It has a thin wrinkled upper valve varying from white to a beautiful golden colour, but the lower valve is greenish or white with an oval hole through it, near to the hinge. Through this opening is a calcified extension of the foot, which fastens the shellfish securely to some solid object such as rock, larger shells, or even wharf piles. The Golden Oyster is found commonly around Auckland and north of Auckland.

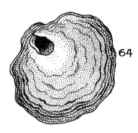

65. Auckland Rock Oyster (Tio)
Saccostrea cucullata

Found only in the upper tidal rocky zone of the northern portion of the North Island and at the Chatham Islands. It cements the lower valve of the shell to the rock and because of its clustering habit assumes varied shapes. A conspicuous feature is the violet to bluish black edging to the shell. This is a much esteemed edible oyster. The season for the marketing of Auckland Rock Oysters is usually from May to about the end of September.

Stewart Island Oyster (Tio Para)
Tiostrea chilensis

Occurs throughout New Zealand and is usually found unattached on mud in shallow water and to a depth of about 30 m. The richest beds of these shellfish are in Foveaux Strait at 20-30 m, where they are extensively dredged by a fleet of small vessels operating from the port of Bluff. (Not figured.)

It has been estimated that an oyster may in the course of one season produce 20-60 million eggs. However, only a small fraction of these ever reaches maturity. If appalling mortality did not take place the oyster would in a few months rank as the world's greatest marine pest. When oysters spawn, eggs and sperms are independently cast adrift in the sea after the manner of most fish. They are at once at the mercy of wind and tides, and the hungry mouths of myriads of other marine creatures. As the survivors develop into their free-swimming stage they are still beset by countless enemies. The few that live to commence adult growth continue to receive attention from predators. The Rock Oyster is troubled by a small univalve, *Lepsiella scobina*, less than 25 mm long, yet capable of drilling a hole through the oyster's shell and devouring the animal within. Finally, man takes his toll of the adults for food.

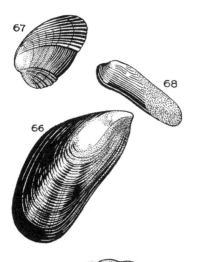

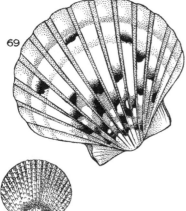

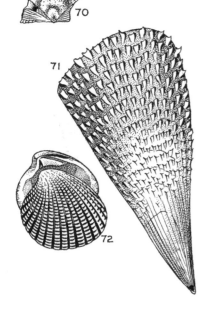

66. Common Mussel (Kuku)
Perna canaliculus

The large greenish mussel so abundant in the North Island. In the South Island the common species is the small bluish-black *Mytilus aoteanus*. The largest and finest mussels are fished commercially from deep-water beds off Coromandel.

67. Nesting Mussel (Kuku Weu)
Modiolarca impacta

An oval, rather inflated mussel 25-40 mm long. Found under stones at low tide throughout New Zealand. It forms a nest of fibrous threads which completely covers the shell.

68. Date Mussel (Taitaki)
Zelithophaga truncata

This is about 50 mm long and has a thick, reddish-brown epidermis. This mussel bores into soft mudstone, aided by an acid secretion which does not dissolve the shell because of the thick horny outer covering. Date mussels are common in the mudstone tidal platform at Cheltenham and the Takapuna Coast, Auckland.

69. Queen Scallop (Tīpā)
Pecten novaezelandiae

This is the large scallop with one valve convex and the other one flat. They occur throughout New Zealand on muddy and sandy flats at low tide and in deeper water. They are very abundant in places on the mud banks of the Manukau Harbour. This scallop swims by suddenly closing the shell with a snap which sends out a jet of water that propels the shellfish forwards. Queen Scallops are our most delicately flavoured shellfish.

70. Fan Scallop (Kopakopa)
Chlamys zelandiae

A small scaly ribbed shell of two equally convex valves. It is brilliantly coloured – lemon-yellow, red-orange, lilac, purple or delicate greys, and is one of the most attractive shells of the New Zealand beaches. Living examples are obtained by turning over boulders at low tide. The shell is fastened to the rock by several strong threads which are associated with the foot of the animal. This scallop is frequently covered with living sponge. Stewart Island examples are much larger and just as brilliantly coloured, but are a different species, *Chlamys dieffenbachi*.

71. Horse Mussel (Hururoa)
Atrina pectinata zelandica

Like a half closed fan, grows to 300-450 mm long. The shell is thin, covered with hollow spines, and is purplish-black with a metallic lustre at the narrow end and inside. This mussel lives about three-quarters buried, point downwards in soft mud, from low tide to about 40 m.

72. Purple Cockle (Karoro)
Venericardia purpurata

Grows to about 40 mm in diameter. It is pinkish to light brown on the outside, which has heavy banded radial ribs, and pinkish to reddish purple within. It lives below low tide to a few metres off many of our sandy coastal beaches. They wash ashore in numbers at Oneroa, Waiheke Island. South Island specimens usually lack the bright pink and purple coloration.

73. Large Wedge Shell (Hanikura)
Macomona liliana

Grows to 60 mm across and is common throughout New Zealand on sandy coastal beaches. Note how the shell is flexed or twisted along the straight upper margin. This species is common at extreme low tide on Cheltenham Beach, Auckland.

74. Triangle Shell (Kaikaikaroro)
Spisula aequilatera
Grows to about 50 mm in diameter. Four of these shells placed tops to the centre make a perfect circle. It washes ashore in great abundance on our ocean beaches, particularly from Waikanae to Wanganui.

75. Oval Trough Shell (Ruheruhe)
Cyclomactra ovata
Grows up to 60 mm long, is inflated, thin and fragile. It lives buried in soft mud within harbours and estuaries.

76. Tuatua
Paphies subtriangulata
Very abundant on coastal sandy beaches of the northern half of the North Island. It is white and solid, 60-80 mm long and can be distinguished from the common Pipi by the position of the apex of the shell, which is not central. It resembles the Toheroa in shape, but is always smaller, more solid, and the valves fit tightly all round. In the Toheroa the shell gapes slightly at each end. The Tuatua has an excellent flavour, sweeter than the Toheroa.

77. Toheroa
Paphies ventricosa
Grows to 150 mm long. It burrows deeply in sand on exposed beaches that are backed by extensive sand dunes. Freshwater seepage from lagoons in the dunes promotes the growth of diatoms and affords a rich inshore concentration of plankton upon which the Toheroa feeds. The largest beds of Toheroas are on Muriwai Beach, the west coast near Dargaville and Ninety Mile Beach. The Toheroa has long been esteemed as a food, but unfortunately the beds have become depleted.

78. Pipi
Paphies australis
The common elongated species with the apex in the middle. It is abundant in sandy or silty mud in harbours. This species was a favourite food of the old time Māori, and vast heaps of the shells can be seen in many districts adjacent to former Māori villages.

79. Lance-shaped Mactra (Pipi Rahi)
Resania lanceolata
This is smooth and polished with two internal strengthening ridges. It grows to about 100 mm long and lives in clean sand below tide off the ocean beaches.

80. Scimitar-shaped Mactra (Pipi Roa)
Zenatia acinaces
Resembles the previous species, but has the apex towards one end. It is of similar size to *Resania*, and lives under the same conditions.

81. Tuangi
Austrovenus stutchburyi
Well known as the New Zealand "cockle", but is not a true cockle. Venus Shell, or the Māori name, Tuangi, are preferable. The Tuangi grows to 50 mm wide and is white with a violet-coloured blotch on the inside of each valve. It lives in large colonies just beneath the surface in muddy localities from mid-tide to low tide, and occasionally to a depth of 5 m. It is esteemed as food.

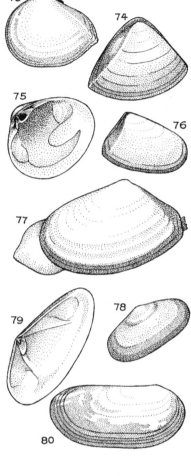

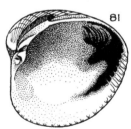

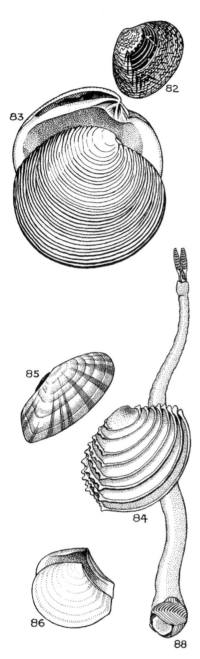

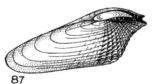

82. Morning Star (Tāwera)
Tawera spissa

A small venerid about 25 mm long, very abundant on most of our northern sandy beaches. It is conspicuously marked with reddish-brown radiate bands and zigzag lines in varied patterns. Tāwera is the Māori name for Venus as morning star.

83. Ringed Dosinia (Harihari)
Dosinia anus

A large, rather thickened and flat disc-shaped shell, coarsely sculptured with concentric sharp ridges. It grows to 80 mm across and is common washed ashore on sandy coastal beaches. It lives buried in sand below low tide. A slightly smaller more inflated species with smooth and finer concentric ridges is *Dosinia subrosea*. A third species, *Dosinia lambata*, little more than 25 mm across, is thin-shelled and looks practically smooth.

84. Frilled Venerid (Pūkauri)
Bassina yatei

About the size of the common Tuangi but less inflated. It is cream-coloured with a violet-tinged tip and has beautiful thin ridges standing out from the surface, often frilled at the edges. The purpose of these ridges is to anchor the shellfish in the sand, for it is not an active burrower. The species lives buried in fine clean sand on coastal beaches at and below low tide.

85. Sunset Shell (Takarepo)
Gari lineolata

A smooth, rather fragile bivalve growing up to 80 mm long. It is brilliant coloured with concentric bands of pink and reddish purple, often overlaid with radiate bands of violet. It comes ashore fairly frequently on coastal sandy beaches and may be found alive at low water in some localities, burrowing into clean sand. A more abundant species, *Gari stangeri*, is less elongated and although dull on the outside has the inside of the shell violet to deep purple.

86. Large Myadora (Pākira)
Myadora striata

A curious white bivalve 25 mm or more across, notable for having one valve convex and the other perfectly flat. The inside of the shell is slightly pearly. It lives partly buried in fine sand at low water on coastal beaches.

87. Rock Borer (Pātiotio)
Barnea similis

Grows to 100 mm long. It is very common around Auckland, where it burrows completely out of sight into the soft mudstone of many of the tidal platforms. The ridges on the shell wear away the rock as the animal moves its shell. A shelly plate in addition to the two normal valves serves to protect the ligament which hinges the shell. *Barnea* is gaping at the larger end of the shell but a related species, *Pholadidea spathulata*, somewhat smaller, is closed in front.

88. Shipworm (Korotupa)
Teredo antarctica

This is scarcely recognisable as a shellfish. The long fleshy tube consists largely of the siphons which bring food to the animal. The shell is a tiny structure at the thickened end of the body. *Teredo* is found only in timber, which it riddles with holes up to nearly 10 mm in diameter and sometimes almost 300 mm long. It does great destruction to wharf piles and the hulls of wooden ships. The New Zealand native timber most resistant to Shipworm attack is Totara.

89. Deep Burrower (Hohehohe)
Panopea zelandica
A large bivalve 80-100 mm long, remarkable for the gaping opening at one end, which allows the extension of the animal into a long, much thickened covering for the siphon tubes. *Panopea* lives 200-400 mm below the surface of sand at low tide on many of our coastal beaches. The long siphons reach the surface of the sand, enabling the animal to sift organic food from the sea and at the same time to lie hidden deeply below the surface. It is seldom taken alive, but the shells frequently wash ashore.

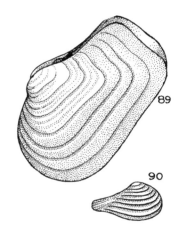

90. Traill's Pointed Clam (Pāpāua Huna)
Cuspidaria trailli
A small shell, quite rare and obtainable by dredging. It is remarkable for having the gill filaments fused into the form of a pump.

Univalves

The Māori name for univalves is papa moana tahi.

91. Pāua
Haliotis iris
Grows to 150 mm in diameter, and is one of our most handsome shells. It is at once recognised by its large, oval, flattened shell, the row of holes along the back and wonderful internal lustre of opalescent greens and blues, with occasional fiery flashes. The shape of the Pāua is a special adaptation for clinging to flat surfaces of rock, after the manner of a limpet; the holes in the shell being for the purpose of expelling water used in the aeration of the gills. The Pāua is found at lowest spring tide level, and in deeper water, on rocky ground in open coastal situations. It is seldom exposed to view and the rough encrusted exterior of the shell renders it almost indistinguishable from its surroundings. Pāuas cling to the rock with great suction, and a quick deft thrust with a broad thin-bladed knife is necessary to prise them off. They favour deep low tidal rock pools, undersides of boulders, beneath ledges and in narrow channels and crevices in the rock. The best localities for the Pāua are Great Barrier Island, the Wellington coast, Kaikoura, Stewart Island and the Chatham Islands.

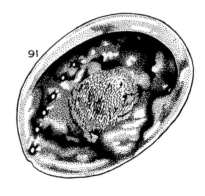

The Pāua animal has a considerable food value and is very palatable, provided the following rather drastic culinary preparations are attended to: Remove the animal from its shell and discard all the soft parts, leaving only the tough foot and muscle, and taking care that a long white ribbon-like structure is removed from the mouth. This is the dental apparatus, which is studded with hundreds of hard, sharp, tiny teeth. If you do not like the black appearance of the animal, this coating will rub off with a coarse rag, leaving the flesh a dirty white or blue-grey colour. Next place the animal inside a cloth and pound it with a heavy piece of wood or the flat of a hammer, just sufficiently to relax the muscular tension.
The Pāua is now rolled in flour or covered with batter and grilled for three minutes. Omit the pounding, or grill for more than three minutes and the Pāua becomes as tough as old leather. Species related to our Pāua are highly esteemed in other countries, particularly in California (where it is known as Abalone), Japan (known as Ear-shell) and Guernsey Island (known as Ormer). The Pāua was almost a staple food with the old time Māori people, who used the shell also to great effect in their carvings and in the making of fishing spinners. Pāua shell is now much sought after for the manufacture of souvenirs.

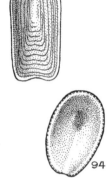

92. *Silvery Paua* (Hihiwa)
Haliotis australis

This is 80-100 mm in diameter and is readily distinguished from the large paua by the silvery iridescent internal lustre of the shell, strong cross ridges and the colour of the animal. It is found together with *iris*, but is not so common. The animal is black with a dark grey foot in *iris*; black with an orange foot in *australis*, and black with a dirty-white foot in *virginea*, the next species.

Virgin Paua (Marapeka)
Haliotis virginea

This is 25-60 mm in diameter and is more brilliantly iridescent than either of the above-mentioned species. It is comparatively rare although distributed from the North Cape to Stewart Island. Two subspecies are known, *morioria* from the Chatham Islands and *huttoni* from the Auckland Islands. (Not figured.)

93. *Shield Shell* (Rori)
Scutus antipodes

An internal shell just sufficient to protect the vital organs of the animal, which is a large black slug very like a Pāua animal minus its shell. *Scutus* belongs to the same family as the slit-limpets, but instead of a slit the shell has a broad shallow notch shown at the lower margin. The shell is solid, white, up to 50 mm long, but the animal grows to 80-130 mm long. It lives under boulders at low tide in clean-water coastal situations through the North and South Islands.

94. *Grooved Limpet* (Ngākihi)
Tugali elegans

Not a true limpet but another relative of the slit-limpets. It has a solid white shell, up to 60 mm long, brownish on the outside and criss-crossed with delicate ridges. The edge is crenulated or delicately toothed, and the inside smooth with a shallow groove. The animal is a large, yellow to orange mass, which when expanded almost envelops the shell. It is widely distributed in New Zealand and lives under boulders at low tide in clean-water coastal localities.

95. *Slit Limpet* (Ngākihi Hahae)
Emarginula striatula

Grows up to 20 mm long and is at once recognised by the deep cut in the margin of the shell. It is widely distributed in New Zealand, but is not common. Living specimens are sometimes found by pulling up seaweeds at extreme low tide.

96. *Key-hole Limpet* (Ngākihikihi)
Monodilepas monilifera

Grows up to 20 mm in diameter and is conspicuous on account of the keyhole-shaped opening in the apex of the shell. It is of deep-water occurrence and is often obtained, along with other shells, in the stomach of the Blue Cod. This species occurs at Stewart Island, but there is a related species at the Chatham Islands and further deep-water representatives off Otago Heads and at Cape Maria van Diemen.

97. *Opal Top-shell* (Matangongo)
Cantharidus opalus

A most beautiful shell, reminiscent of a tropical beach rather than of our cool seas. It grows to 40 mm high and lives on the fronds of kelp at and below low tide. The colour pattern is of delicate zigzag lines and stripes of purple on a blue ground. The inside of the aperture reflects light in the manner of a magnificent fire opal. Cook Strait and Stewart Island are the best areas for this species. A smaller and more common bright pink relative is *Cantharidus purpureus*.

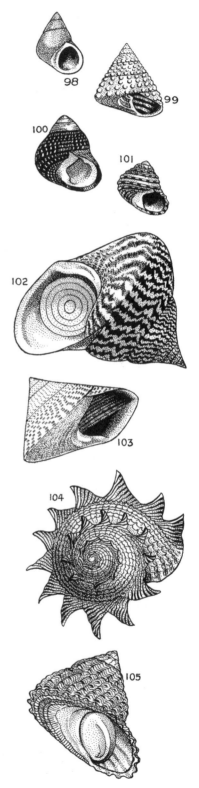

98. Small Opal Shell (Matamatangongo)
Micrelenchus dilatatus

This is scarcely 10 mm high, but the interior of the shell is even more brilliantly opalescent than in the previous species. The outside of the shell is russet to red-brown with a few pale dots. It is common living on seaweeds at low tide on the open coast.

99. Greenish Top-shell (Tihipu)
Trochus viridis

Grows to 20 mm high and occurs commonly at low tide in rocky situations on the open coast. The top bears rather large rounded knobs, but the base is flat, spirally lined and grooved. It is white to greenish, but usually the top is encrusted. Dead shells on the beach show a pearly undercoating as the surface layer flakes off.

100. Dark Top-shell (Maihi)
Melagraphia aethiops

Grows to 25 mm high and is one of the most abundant species of the coastal rocks throughout New Zealand. It is easily recognised by the pattern of spiral rows of white-chequered patches on a dull purplish-black ground.

101. Mudflat Top-shell (Whētiko)
Diloma rostrata

Smaller than *aethiops* and has a few strong spiral ridges and wavy dull purplish bands on a yellowish-white ground. This species is common on the mudflats of the North and South Islands.

102. Tiger Shell (Maurea)
Calliostoma tigris

Grows to 80 mm in diameter and is at once recognised by its delicately tapered spire and conspicuous pattern of zigzag reddish-brown radiating bands. It lives under boulders in clean-water sheltered situations, but is nowhere common. Whangarei Heads, Mount Maunganui and West Haven Inlet (Nelson) are good localities for this handsome species.

103. Pale Tiger Shell (Reoreo)
Calliostoma selectum

Smaller than *tigris* and distinguished by its pale yellowish-brown colour pattern and sharply-keeled edge of the shell. It lives in shallow water off our ocean beaches and frequently washes ashore in larger numbers. They are especially abundant on the west coast beaches of Wellington Province, from Waikanae to Wanganui.

104. Circular Saw Shell (Ripo Matamata)
Astraea heliotropium

This requires no description. It occurs throughout New Zealand in moderately deep water. Dead shells wash ashore on ocean beaches, but living ones are obtainable only by dredging.

105. Cook's Turban Shell (Karaka)
Cookia sulcata

This is related to the above species but is quite common. It lives under rocky ledges, at low tide, in clean-water coastal situations. In life the shell is dull and encrusted, but when the outer coating flakes off a beautiful pearly under layer is revealed. The aperture is stoppered with a strong shelly oval operculum.

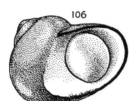

106

106. *Cat's Eye* (Ataata)
Turbo smaragdus
Best known of all our shells of the intertidal rocks. It feeds on seaweeds and lives in the mid-tidal belt of the grape-seaweed, *Hormosira*. It sometimes grows to over 50 mm in diameter. The circular greenish operculum, the cat's eye, is its most conspicuous feature.

107

107. *Wheel Shell* (Kota)
Zethalia zelandica
A small, flattened, solidly-built shell distinguished by a radiate pattern of dark reddish-brown, like the spokes of a wheel. It lives at and below low tide on ocean beaches. They are particularly abundant on the beaches south of Whangarei Heads.

108. *Black Nerita* (Matangarahu)
Nerita atramentosa
Grows to about 25 mm in diameter and is abundant in the northern parts of New Zealand on the rocky upper tidal belt. It has a tightly-fitting operculum with a projection which acts as a hinge. A related species of the West Indies is the well-known "Bleeding Tooth".

108

109

109. *Fragile Limpet* (Tūpere)
Atalacmea fragilis
Lives under smooth stones between tides in clean-water situations. It is about 10 mm in diameter and has a pattern of concentric brown rings on a green ground.

110. *Encrusted Limpet* (Rūharu)
Patelloida corticata
A small flat limpet, more or less star-shaped, which is found at extreme low tide on the open rocky coast. The encrusted shell is almost indistinguishable from the surroundings.

110

111. *Black-edged Limpet* (Ngākihi Po)
Notoacmea pileopsis
Lives on exposed rocks towards high tide. It is mottled greyish-green on the back and bluish-white inside with a black border and a brownish central area.

111

112. *Radiate Limpet* (Ngākihi)
Cellana radians
The common northern limpet. It grows to 50 mm long and has a great variety of colour markings; anything from plain silvery-grey to an intricate tortoise-shell design in yellow and rich reddish-brown. At Wellington the common limpet is *Cellana denticulata*, at Dunedin, *Cellana strigilis redimiculum*, and at points along the East Coast from north of Dunedin to East Cape the beautiful orange-coloured *Cellana flava* may be found. The best localities for *flava* are Kaikoura coast and Napier.

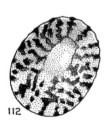

113

112

113. *Periwinkle* (Ngaeti)
Nodilittorina antipodum
A most abundant shell on high tidal rocks throughout New Zealand. It seldom grows larger than 10 mm and is bluish white with a broad spiral band of bright blue. This shellfish lives at extreme high water mark, where it is reached by salt spray only for a brief period each day. It feeds on an inconspicuous dark grey lichen. This is a true periwinkle, but that name is frequently applied to other shellfish, some of the top-shells and the Cat's Eye.

awtPowell

114. Horn Shell *(Koeti)*
Zeacumantus lutulentus
Grows to about 20 mm long and is extremely abundant on mud flats of the northern parts of New Zealand.

115. Turret Shell *(Papatai)*
Maoricolpus roseus
This is 30-50 mm long and lives from low tide to moderately deep water. Where conditions are favourable they occur in vast beds. Beds off Devonport, Auckland Harbour, in 10-15 m, are so prolific that there are several hundreds of these shells to each square metre. The shell is a mottled reddish-brown.

116. Corkscrew *(Papa Hurihuri)*
Tenagodus weldii
This shell, which is 50-60 mm long, is loosely coiled and has an open slit running up one side. It lives embedded in sponge, and is obtained only by dredging, or when a piece of sponge containing a colony of them is cast ashore. *Tenagodus* is one of the Siliquariidae, the wormshells, but the other members of this group are difficult to distinguish from the serpulids which construct similar masses of shelly tubes.

117. Ostrich Foot *(Totorere)*
Struthiolaria papulosa
A fine shell up to 80 mm long, conspicuous for its strong white lip to the aperture and radiate pattern of reddish-brown bands. It lives half buried in sand on coastal beaches. Its name is derived from an alleged resemblance of the foot of the animal to that of an Ostrich.

118. Carrier Shell *(Papa Kotakota)*
Xenophora neozelanica
A rare deep-water species of the northern part of the North Island. It is a wonderful example of the application of camouflage in shellfish. To evade detection the Carrier Shell cements to the back of its shell bits and pieces of rock or shell from the surrounding debris of the sea-bottom. It even selects odd valves of bivalves and cements them with the concave side uppermost, thus emphasizing their emptiness to prowling carnivorous fish. The Carrier Shell is about 80 mm across and lives in 40-90 m.

119. White Slipper Shell *(Ngākihi Tea)*
Crepidula monoxyla
A limpet-shaped shell, up to 40 mm long, with a curious internal shelf. It lives attached to large shells and assumes a variety of shapes according to the convex or concave nature of the base of attachment.

120. Ribbed Slipper Shell *(Ngākihi Hiwihiwi)*
Crepidula costata
Similar to the previous species but stronger and prominently ribbed. It is found on the backs of mussel shells and also on the undersides of rocks at low tide.

121. Circular Slipper Shell *(Ngākihi Kōpio)*
Sigapatella novaezelandiae
This grows to 30 mm in diameter and is also found attached to mussel shells. It has a light brown epidermis and is white with a reddish-brown to violet-coloured patch inside. The spire is off-centre in *Sigapatella*, but centrally placed in the related but smaller *Zegalerus tenuis*.

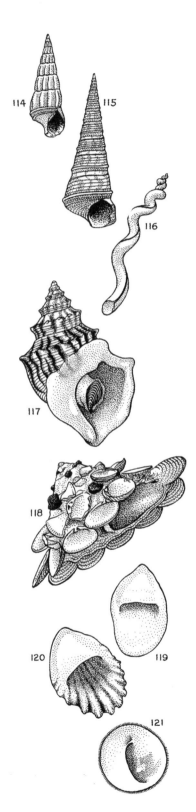

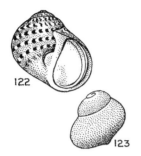

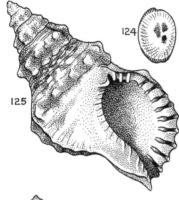

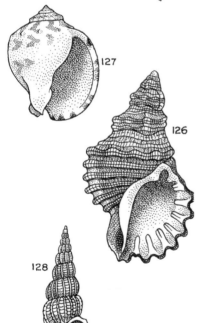

122. Necklace Shell (Ngaere)
Tanea zelandica
About 25 mm in diameter, it has a beautiful pattern of reddish-brown markings on a light brown to white polished surface. It lives on the open coast in sandy localities, but is seldom found alive. The operculum is white and shelly, completely sealing the aperture. It is a carnivorous species and employs its teeth (radula) to drill holes in the shells of its victims.

123. Violet Snail (Kararua)
Janthina janthina
Resembles the Garden Snail in size and shape, but in colour it is brilliant violet. It lives on the surface of the ocean, off-shore, and vast numbers are frequently washed up on our coastal beaches after storms. The animal constructs a small raft of imprisoned air bubbles to which the egg capsules are attached. A specimen taken at Muriwai, Auckland west coast, had 70 egg capsules attached to the raft; each capsule contained 500 young which makes a total of 35,000 embryos for each raft. A smaller species seldom more than 10 mm high is *Janthina exigua*, and a smooth one that glistens as though it was newly varnished is *Janthina globosa*. They are common in the north, but become scarce as one travels southward.

124. New Zealand Cowry (Awatai)
Trivia merces
This is about 10 mm long with a group of pink blotches on the top of the shell, and is our sole representative of a family very well represented in all tropical countries. The New Zealand species is very scarce. Dead shells wash ashore occasionally at Cape Maria van Dieman, Ahipara and Mount Maunganui.

125. Large Trumpet Shell (Awanui)
Charonia lampas rubicunda
Grows to about 200 mm long and is found adjacent to rocks near the entrance to harbours in many localities from Tauranga northwards. They are fairly abundant, especially in spring, when they come into shallow water to breed, at Mount Maunganui and Whangarei Heads.

126. Spengler's Trumpet Shell (Pupakapaka)
Cabestana spengleri
Smaller than the preceding species, it is strongly spirally corrugated and knobbed and has a dense golden-brown pile-like epidermis. It favours the quiet waters of harbours and lives around boulders and under rock ledges of reefs in the proximity of mud-flats.

127. Helmet Shell (Pūpū Māeneene)
Semicassis pyrum
Grows 50-60 mm long. A handsome smooth shell with a row of small knobs around the shoulder. The colouring is pale yellowish-brown to pinkish with revolving series of reddish-brown blotches. The animal has a horny operculum shaped like an open fan. It is found on sandy beaches of the open coast from low water to deeper water. At times it washes ashore in numbers on the Bay of Plenty beaches, Port Waikato and Waikanae Beach.

128. Wentle-trap (Tōtoro)
Cirsotrema zelebori
A charming little white shell up to 25 mm long with a long tapered spire sculptured with regular vertical ridges crossed by finer spirals. They wash ashore on sandy beaches of the east coast, particularly in the Bay of Plenty.

129. Cask Shell *(Pūpū Tangimoana)*
Tonna cerevisina

This is very large and thin, sculptured with strong spiral corrugations. It grows to 230 mm high and has a very large aperture. Occasionally these shells wash ashore on North Auckland beaches, but they live on sandy or muddy bottoms in 25-50 m.

130. Siphon Whelk *(Kākara Nui)*
Penion cuvierianus

Common in the northern part of the North Island on rocky reefs at low tide. It is usually rugged and encrusted and grows to about 130 mm long. It is a solid brownish or greyish shell spirally ridged and lined in dark brown. Note the long canal, a feature of most carnivorous species. The southern relative, *Penion sulcatus*, is spirally ridged but lacks the nodular shoulder.

131. Knobbed Whelk *(Kākara)*
Austrofusus glans

This is less than half the size of the Siphon Whelk and has a thin shell gaily painted with vertical wavy bands of reddish-brown on a white base. It lives at and below low tide on open sandy beaches. This species is abundant in the Bay of Plenty, Waikanae to the Manawatu River and at Golden Bay, Nelson.

132. Lined Whelk *(Huamutu)*
Buccinulum pallidum powelli

Grows to 40 mm long and is distinctly marked with clean-cut purple-brown lines on a white surface. It is found under stones at low tide on coastal reefs in the northern part of the North Island. There are about 30 more or less closely allied species of this group in New Zealand. A similar species, *Buccinulum linea*, lives in the South Island.

133. Speckled Whelk *(Kāwari)*
Cominella adspersa

Abundant in the North Island, particularly on rocky ground, near mud, in harbours. It is an active carnivorous species and groups of them are a common sight feeding on the Tuangi *(Austrovenus stutchburyi)*. The Speckled Whelk grows to 50 mm high, but a much smaller species, *Cominella glandiformis*, is even more common and certainly more widely distributed.

134. Spiny Murex *(Pūpū Tarataratea)*
Poirieria zelandica

A handsome long-spined white shell up to 50 mm high. It is often washed ashore on coastal beaches, but the best specimens are found only in deep water. These shells often become tangled in the nets of fishing vessels.

135. Octagonal Murex *(Pūpū Taratara)*
Murexul octogonus

A rugged, more or less eight-sided shell, with short curved spines. It is dull purplish-brown, up to 50 mm high and found under stones at low tide in clean-water situations. Good specimens are found at Rangitoto Island, Auckland. A smaller and differently shaped murex, *Pterotyphis eos*, is a highly prized rarity, occasionally found at the Bay of Islands. It is a glorious pink, and hence the name *eos*, in reference to the Greek goddess of the dawn.

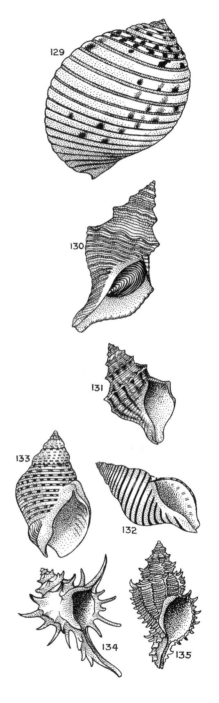

136. **White Rock Shell** (Hopetea)
Dicathais orbita

A thick, coarse, spirally-ridged white shell up to 90 mm high. It is common amongst rocks at low tide, both in harbours and on the open coast. The egg cases are deposited on the sides of boulders and in caverns. They are crowded together, honeycomb fashion, are of cream to lilac colour, and each has a pin-hole in the top. The larval shell which emerges from the egg is an efficient free-swimmer. Hence the species is widespread in New Zealand and occurs in Tasmania and southern Australia also.

137. **Dark Rock Shell** (Ngāeo)
Haustrum haustorium

Smaller and thinner-shelled than the previous species, and easily recognised by the large open mouth with a conspicuous brown patch within the aperture. It is an active carnivorous species and has been known to force open oysters and other bivalves by inserting the lip of its own shell as a wedge.

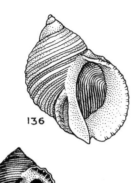
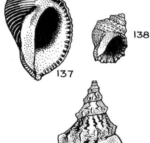
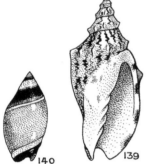

138. **Oyster Borer** (Kaikai Tio)
Lepsiella scobina

This is less than 25 mm high, but plays havoc on local rock oyster beds. The animal uses its teeth (the radula) to drill holes through the oyster's shell and then extracts the oyster piecemeal. It may take 45 minutes to pierce the thick shell of an adult oyster.

139. **Arabic Volute** (Pūpū Rore)
Alcithoe arabica

Grows to about 150 mm high. Distinguished by the spiral folds on the pillar or axis of the shell, strong tubercles on the shoulder and bold pattern of reddish-brown zigzag stripes and blotches. This volute lives half buried in sand at low tide and in deeper water on the coastal beaches. Another species, *Alcithoe swainsoni*, is commonly found in the North and South Islands. It is more elongated, has less colour and lacks the shoulder and strong tubercles. The egg of *Alcithoe* is a white opaque dome about 10 mm in diameter. It is usually cemented to some other shell.

140. **Southern Olive** (Pūpū Pīataata)
Amalda australis

A handsome polished shell up to 40 mm high. It is bluish-slate around the middle and dark brown both on the spire and on the base. *Amalda* lives buried under little mounds of sand on our coastal beaches. There are six New Zealand species, but *australis* is the one most frequently seen. It is common at Pilot Bay, Tauranga Harbour, where fine large examples occur.

141. **Notched Tower Shell** (Torire)
Phenatoma rosea

This is characteristic of the many New Zealand species of the family Turridae, most of which have a pronounced cleft or sinus in the outer lip. None of the species are really common and most of them are of deep-water occurrence. The figured one is about 25 mm high, of delicate rose colour, and is found occasionally at and below low tide on coastal sandy beaches.

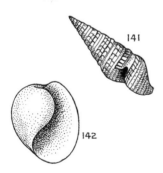

142. **White Bubble Shell** (Pūpū Tuatea)
Haminoea zelandiae

Very thin and frail, 10-20 mm in diameter. It occurs partially embedded in the folds of a soft greenish slug-like animal, which lives on the green Sea-grass beds of the northern mudflats.

143. Oval Bubble Shell *(Pūpū Waharoa)*
Bulla quoyii
Twice the size of *Haminoea*, more solid, and light brown, marbled with reddish-brown. Empty shells frequently wash ashore on harbour beaches, but living examples are seldom seen.

144. Sea Butterfly *(Pūpū Kopae)*
Cavolinia tridentata
A small fragile inhabitant of the open seas, which washes ashore at rare intervals on our ocean beaches. The Sea Butterfly is a pteropod (wing-footed), which name refers to the expansion of the foot of the animal into two spreading lobes used for swimming.

145. Warty Sea Slug *(Rori)*
Archidoris wellingtonensis
A large orange-coloured slug covered on the back with numerous round blisters. Note the circle of feathery gills at the back and the two club-shaped organs of smell at the front end. There are about 50 species of sea slugs in New Zealand seas, all of which are soft-bodied, but a few have an internal shell remnant. Sea slugs or nudibranchs (naked gills) often have most brilliant colours, but unfortunately there is no means as yet discovered of preserving them satisfactorily.

146. Feathery Sea Hare *(Rori Tararua)*
Bursatella glauca
A greenish soft slug about 80 mm long. It has a cleft in the back from which a purple fluid is ejected when the animal is molested. This provides the equivalent of a "smoke screen" to enable the animal to escape under cover. The true sea hares (*Aplysia*) have a flat internal shell-remnant, which is little more than a membrane. *Bursatella* has become extremely abundant in Orakei Basin, Auckland, since the tidal waters have been impounded by the railway embankment.

147. Siphon Limpet *(Ngākihi Awaawa)*
Siphonaria australis
Not a true limpet, but an interesting example of a highly developed pulmonate or air-breathing shellfish, akin to a land snail, which has reverted to the limpet shape to suit its environment. These false limpets are distinguished by a deep internal groove at one side of the shell which leads to the opening of the lung. *Siphonaria australis* is about 20 mm in diameter and lives attached to rocks, high up in the inter-tidal zone. A large southern species 50 mm long is *Benhamina obliquata*.

148. Mud Snail *(Tītiko)*
Amphibola crenata
This is about 20 mm in diameter and is found in thousands high up on most tidal mudflats through New Zealand. Its most interesting feature is that it is the only pulmonate snail with an operculum. It is an esteemed Māori food.

149. Filhol's Ear Shell *(Anga Niho)*
Marinula filholi
A small, high-tidal, air-breathing shellfish found under rocks and decaying seaweed in the zone of the Glass-wort, *Salicornia*. Note the teeth-like projections inside the aperture, which give a resemblance to the human ear.

150. Banded Ear Shell *(Anga Nui Niho)*
Ophicardelus costellaris
This is larger than *Marinula*, but does not exceed 13 mm high. It belongs to the high tidal fauna also and is very common around the northern coastline of New Zealand. It is of dull brownish colour with reddish-brown spiral bands.

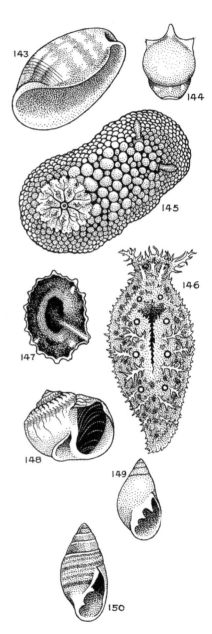

Chitons and Tusk Shells

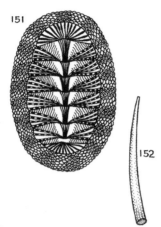

151. Snake's-skin Chiton (Papatua)
Sypharochiton pelliserpentis
This is typical of a separate class of the Mollusca which stands uniformly distinct from all other groups. The shell is always composed of eight movable pieces fastened together by muscles and a surrounding leathery girdle, which is often studded with scales. Variation in the number of valves of the shell is not unknown, but such discrepancy can always be traced to some injury. Chitons are vegetarian feeders, but spend most of their time fastened to rocks by suction. About 50 New Zealand species are known, but many of them are rare. The figured one is a common intertidal species, with well developed girdle scales. One species, *Cryptoconchus porosus*, has beautiful greenish-blue internal valves. These are the "butterflies" so keenly sought by amateur collectors. Our largest species, *Eudoxochiton nobilis*, grows to 114 mm long. Many chitons have interesting composite shell eyes which are actually studded on the valves of the shell and under a high-power lens look like small black dots.

152. Tusk Shell (Kōmore)
Antalis nana
A white, tubular, tapering shell, open at each end and about 25 mm long. It is seldom seen on the beaches, for it lives buried in mud in shallow to moderately deep water. The tusk shells make up still another class of the Mollusca, distinct from all other kinds. These shells were highly prized by the ancient Māori, who threaded them to form necklaces. Antalis is abundant in the Manukau Harbour.

Octopus and Allies

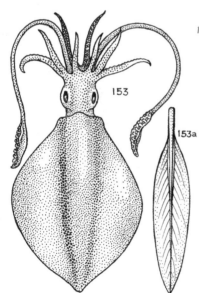

153. Broad Squid (Ngū)
Sepioteuthis australis
A deep-water, soft-bodied mollusc with eight rather short sucker-bearing arms and two long arms. The body extends into a broad flange on each side, and under the skin down the middle, a membranous shell remnant, very like a feather, is found (Fig. 153a). Squids and cuttlefish resemble the octopus except for the long body and their ten arms. The body of the Broad Squid grows to about 250 mm long, but some veritable giants of other species have been found in New Zealand waters. One of these, *Architeuthis longimanus*, 17.5 m in total length, was washed ashore at Lyall Bay, Wellington, in 1881. At times during June and July giant squids are seen off Cape Campbell, Marlborough. They apparently live in deep water and are often attacked by Sperm Whales. No doubt most of the stories of sea-serpents are based upon fleeting glimpses of the writhing arms of giant squids. A fabulous sea creature of Norse mythology, the "Kraken", as well as the famed "Hydra of Lerna", destroyed by Hercules, are simply legendary exaggerations based upon these creatures. The Cuttle-fish resembles the squid except for the more solid internal shell remnant, or cuttle-bone, which is the well-known oval friable object given to caged birds to sharpen and clean their beaks. Living Cuttle-fish have not been found in New Zealand seas, but fragments of the cuttle-bone of the large southern Australian *Sepia apama* wash ashore at times on our northern beaches.

154. *Arrow Squid* (Ngū)
Nototodarus sloanii

This has an arrow-shaped body, 100-200 mm long, and is more often seen than the above species. Sometimes, especially at night, they are encountered by people spearing flat-fish on tidal mudflats. This species has a membranous internal shell remnant also, but it is narrow like a reed. Squids are very fast swimmers and they have no difficulty in capturing crabs and small fish upon which they feed. The squids swim by ejecting a strong jet of water through a funnel-shaped opening.

155. *Ram's Horn Shell* (Kotakota Ngū)
Spirula spirula

This is the white openly-coiled shell about 25 mm long, which washes ashore in great numbers on our west coast beaches. Note the compartments, with pearly partitions, each connected to the next by a tiny tube. This shell is internal in the body cavity of a small squid. *Spirula* lives neither at the surface nor on the sea bottom, but in an intermediate position at depths between 200 and 2000 m. The compartments of the shell are evidently used in some way as air or gas chambers to assist the animal in adapting itself to varying depths.

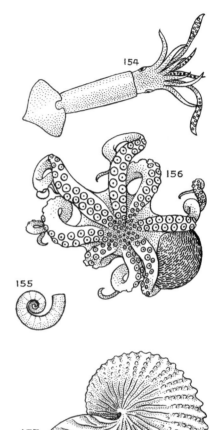

156. *Common Octopus* (Wheke)
Octopus maorum

As the name indicates, the octopus has eight sucker-bearing arms, really legs, since they have been derived from the foot of a normal mollusc. The octopus is entirely without a shell, the only hard parts being a pair of jaws shaped just like a parrot's beak. This is located in the middle of the circle of arms. When fully grown the arms of the octopus are about one metre long, and these creatures can be quite unpleasant if encountered in the vicinity of rocks or seaweed. Swimming is accomplished by forcing a jet of water from the siphon and then catapulting the whole body through the outstretched circle of arms. The octopus feeds mostly on other shellfish, sometimes crawling over a cockle bed and clinging to numbers of these bivalves by means of its sucker-bearing arms. It then crawls back to a cavern or under a rock ledge and settles down to eat the cockles at leisure. If disturbed the octopus clouds the water with an inky fluid, and is then able to make a retreat under cover of the discoloured water. This fluid was the origin of the artists' sepia colour, which was formerly made from the octopus. Another curious feature of the octopus is its ability to change colour at will, for in a few seconds one may be seen to change from dull grey to bright orange.

157. *Paper Nautilus* (Pūpū Tarakihi)
Argonauta nodosa

This is related to the octopus, and the animal is similar in most respects, except that the female produces a delicate pure-white embossed shell, which sometimes reaches 230 mm in diameter. This shell is exclusive to the female, and she uses it to house the egg mass. The male *Argonauta* is completely overshadowed by the female, for he is without a shell, and is seldom more than 25 mm long. The shell is scarcely ever seen on mainland beaches, but at times they come ashore in numbers on the off-shore islands and in the Marlborough Sounds. Some fine specimens have been taken at Great Barrier Island and on Mayor Island.

Land Snails

Land snails are univalve shellfish which have managed to forsake the sea, develop lungs, and live on dry land. In all other respects they are essentially "shellfish". The Māori name for land snails is ngata whenua.

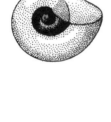

158. *Pūpū Rangi* (Kauri Snail)
Paryphanta busbyi
A North Auckland representative of a group of large carnivorous snails found only in New Zealand, but with near relatives in Tasmania and Victoria. The Pūpū Rangi is coincident in range with the Kauri tree, but there is no relationship between the two – in fact the snail shuns the immediate vicinity of Kauri for the ground there is usually too dry for the existence of worms, upon which the Pūpū Rangi feeds. The shell is a flattened spiral of dark greenish colour, about 60-80 mm in diameter. It lays hard limy-shelled white oval eggs about 12 mm long, which are deposited in nests in the leaf mould of the forest floor (Fig. 158a). About 40 kinds of these large carnivorous snails are now known from New Zealand and they are distributed from North Cape to Southland, but occur mostly west of the dividing range either in rain forest or in subalpine forest and tussock. Some of the South Island species are brilliantly coloured – *Paryphanta superba* grows to 90 mm in diameter and is uniformly khaki, *P. gilliesi* is red-brown like rosewood, *P. lignaria* is alternately dark brown and yellowish in radial stripes and *P. hochstetteri* from the mountain tops of Nelson is variously spirally banded and lined in reddish-brown on a yellowish to light-brown ground. Snails of this type have no difficulty in capturing and eating worms over 200 mm long.

159. *Greenwood's Snail* (Pūpū Nehenehe)
Rhytida greenwoodi
A flattish brown snail about 25 mm in diameter. It is carnivorous, and is widely distributed in the North Island forests from Auckland southwards. There are a number of related species in both islands, but they are mostly smaller. A North Auckland one with a keeled edge is *R. dunniae*.

160. *Pūpū Harakeke* (Flax Snail)
Placostylus hongii
A tall-spired solidly built chocolate to reddish-brown-coloured snail about 75 mm high. Formerly they were abundant along the coastal areas from Whangarei Heads to Whangaroa, but with the clearing of much of the vegetation they now exist only in a few isolated spots. However, the species still lives in great numbers at the Poor Knights Islands, off the North Auckland east coast. These snails are vegetarian and feed largely upon fallen Karaka leaves. They are found hidden under leaves and around sedges, but only in flax when there is no other cover. They lay thin-shelled limy eggs about 5 mm in diameter. Another species, *P. ambagiosus*, with several subspecies, belongs to the Cape Maria van Diemen-North Cape area, and a third, *P. bollonsi*, the largest of them all, is found on Great Island of the Three Kings group. The *Placostylus* snails are significant in tracing ancient land connections, for they occur outside New Zealand only in the Melanesian islands, northwards to the Solomons and eastwards to Fiji. This area of distribution coincides exactly with the now largely submerged "Melanesian Plateau", a complex system of connecting land which at no great depth more or less links the North Auckland Peninsula with these Melanesian Islands. Deep water in the Tasman Sea separates this former land mass from Australia, where no *Placostylus* snails are known.

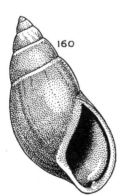

161. *Phrixgnathus celia*

162. *Suteria ide*

These small snails are chosen at random to represent the large number of native species found in our forests. Some occur under fallen leaves on the ground, others under lichens and on ferns and mosses, and a few crawl on the foliage of trees. Almost any patch of undisturbed native bush has snails – it is just a matter of keen sight and concentration to find them, for some are no larger than the head of a pin.

163. *Operculate Snail* (*Hātaretare*)

Liarea hochstetteri carinella

A brownish snail, little more than 7 mm high. It is found on the forest floor under leaves. Its chief interest lies in the fact that it has an operculum and its anatomy indicates that in the distant past it was derived from the marine periwinkles. Most other snails had their origin in ancestors of the marine pulmonates.

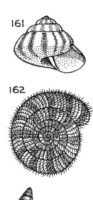
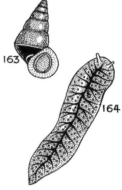

164. *Veined Slug* (*Pūtoko Ropiropi*)

Athoracophorus bitentaculatus

This is a native slug about 40 mm long, of light yellowish colour conspicuously veined like a leaf in reddish-brown. It is found behind the clasping leaf bases of the Nikau Palm, at the bases of flax and under the bark of decaying logs. The common Garden Snail and all the slugs found in cultivated surroundings are not native species but accidental importations from Britain.

Freshwater Shells

Representatives of both the univalves and bivalves have succeeded in adapting to freshwater conditions, but the five other molluscan classes are exclusively marine. The Māori name for freshwater shells is papa wai māori.

165. *Spiny Water Snail* (*Ngata Huru*)

Potamopyrgus antipodarum

A buff-coloured snail about 8 mm long and armed with bristles (form *corolla*). It lives on water weeds in lakes and streams, and is particularly abundant at Lake Pupuke, Auckland.

166. *Dark Water Snail* (*Ngata Pōuri*)

Potamopyrgus antipodarum

Slightly larger than form *corolla*, this form often has a black coating and is always smooth. It is abundant everywhere in fresh and even brackish waters.

167. *Flat Pond Snail* (*Ngata Piripiri*)

Gyraulus corinna

This is little more than 3 mm across. It is often found adhering to the under side of water lily leaves in ponds.

168. *Left-handed Water Snail* (*Ngata Wai Ngaro*)

Glyptophysa variabilis

This grows to slightly more than 10 mm high. It is invariably coiled in a left-handed manner, and is found on aquatic plants in lakes, ponds and drains. A water snail, *Lymnaea tomentosa*, of similar shape to *Glyptophysa*, but smaller and normally coiled, is the local intermediate host for the Liver-fluke which causes sickness and mortality in sheep.

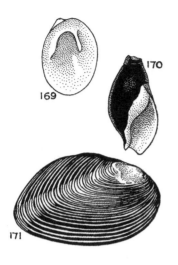

169. Freshwater Limpet (*Piri Toka*)
Latia neritoides
It attains 10 mm in diameter and is found attached to stones in fast running streams. Mostly it is covered with a black coating, and has a curiously shaped internal shelf.

170. Decapitated Water Snail (*Piri Tara Kore*)
Melanopsis trifasciata
This is greenish with several brown spiral bands, or black when adult. It loses the top of the spire with age, due to the erosive acid nature of fresh water. This snail grows to 30 mm high and is found on stones in streams, particularly near the sea under slightly brackish conditions. It is widely but by no means generally distributed in the North Island.

171. Freshwater Mussel (*Kākahi*)
Hydridella menziesi
This, or related species or subspecies, are found buried in mud in most of our lakes, rivers and streams. They grow 50-100 mm long, and are covered with a thick dark green horny epidermis. The interior of the shell is white and pearly. These shellfish have an interesting early stage in which the larval shell attaches itself to the fins or body of a small freshwater fish.

Arthropods

The most successful of the invertebrates are undoubtedly the arthropods. They include the crustaceans, the centipedes, the insects and the spiders; all characterised by having jointed legs and a more or less hard but flexible body-covering, divided into segments.

These creatures have exploited successfully every type of habitat where life can exist. The sea and fresh waters teem with crustaceans, the land has its hordes of insects, spiders and centipedes, while the air vibrates with the flight and drone of innumerable flying insects.

Crustaceans

Crustaceans include shrimps, crayfish, crabs and barnacles. They are best represented in the sea, but there are freshwater and land forms also.

The chief differentiating feature of crustaceans as opposed to other arthropods is the possession of gills and two pairs of antennae. Barnacles appear to be a queer inclusion in this group, since they have an external shell of calcium carbonate. The larval history, however, shows that barnacles originate from shrimp-like creatures. At the conclusion of its free-swimming stage the larval barnacle comes to rest on some solid object, head downwards, and then grows about itself the characteristic limy shell. The feeler-like processes which often protrude from a barnacle are the modified legs now used for raking in food.

Most crustaceans achieve growth by a series of moults. They are able to cast their old armour complete, even to the jointed covering of the legs, just as a hand is withdrawn from a glove.

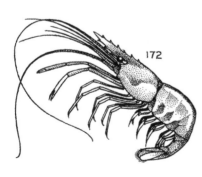

172. Common Shrimp (*Tarawera*)
Palaemon affinis
This attains a length of 40-70 mm and is semi-transparent with green lines on its body and red spots on its legs. It is frequently found in rock pools, darting about with great rapidity when disturbed. Note the serrated lance-like projection on the head. It is very common throughout New Zealand.

173. Snapping Shrimp (*Kōwhitiwhiti Moana*)
Alpheus novaezealandiae
About the same size as the Common Shrimp, but is at once distinguished by the large unevenly developed "chelae" or claws. The movable finger of the large claw makes a distinctly audible snap when the animal operates the claw. The colouring is opaque green, yellowish-brown or dull blue mottled with white. It is found under stones, resting on mud at low tide; but also lives in mud burrows.

174. Shield Shrimp (*Kouraura Wai Māori*)
Lepidurus viridis
Found in freshwater ponds, puddles and ditches throughout the South Island and occasionally in the North Island. It is usually seen in early spring, particularly in Canterbury, and occurs mostly in waters of a temporary nature. The Shield Shrimp is thin, semi-transparent greenish, about 40 mm long and bears some resemblance to the large *Limulus* or Horse-shoe Crab of China Seas and the Atlantic seaboard of North America. There is no close relationship, however. *Lepidurus* has a thin sub-circular shield over the forward part of the body and 60 pairs of swimming legs underneath.

175. Sea Centipede (*Weri Moana*)
Batedotea elongatus
A slender crustacean of the order known as Isopoda, the same group that contains the common Wood-louse of our gardens. It grows up to 50 mm long and is coloured brown in harmony with the intertidal seaweeds upon which it lives. A bright green species *Paridotea ungulata* is found on the green Sea-lettuce. It is very widely distributed, occurring from the Auckland Islands to Akaroa, and abroad it has been recorded from Australia to the Falkland Islands. Other species are known from the South Island and subantarctic islands.

176. Sandhopper (*Namu Māwhitiwhiti*)
Corophium acutum
This species, from 6-8 m in Dunedin Harbour, serves to illustrate the order Amphipoda of which a large number of New Zealand species is known. These are the tiny shrimp-like hoppers which abound under decaying seaweed on our sandy beaches. Both the amphipods and the isopods are good scavengers and serve to keep the beaches clean. If you kick aside a patch of decaying seaweed on a sandy beach the acrobats amongst the disturbed creatures are the amphipods, the scuttlers the isopods. Our most abundant sea-beach amphipods belong to the genus *Talorchestia*. Some are of freshwater occurrence and others live entirely on land quite remote from the sea. A common species found under decaying leaves in gardens is *Parorchestia sylvicola*.

177. Armoured Isopod (*Kutu Moana*)
Isocladus armatus
A small species common in rock pools around our whole coastline. It varies in colour from dull brown to greenish white. Two other isopods, *Limnoria* and *Sphaeroma*, together with the amphipod *Chelura*, combine with the shellfish *Teredo* in the destruction of wharf piles and other marine timber structures. Another small isopod *Cirolana* sp. has the annoying habit of biting one's legs if one stands still too long in shallow water.

"Whale-feed" (Uraura), as applied in New Zealand, refers to the larval stage of several species of crustaceans. Masses of reddish-purple "whale-feed" frequently wash ashore in summer on North Auckland east coast beaches. In Cook Strait and off the east coast of the South Island "whale-feed" commonly occurs in such vast concentrations that pinkish or bluish patches on the surface of the sea are visible from a distance. The Squat Lobster *Munida gregaria* can be one of the principle species occurring in these swarms. (Not figured.)

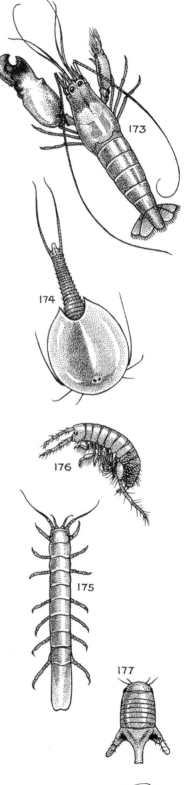

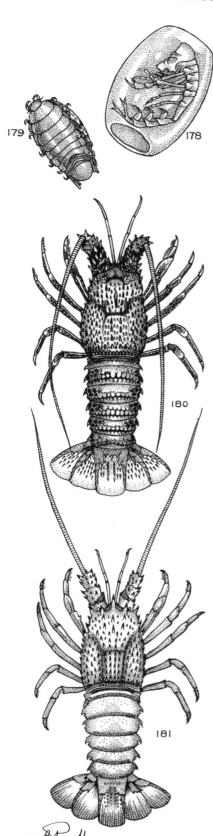

178. Barrel Shrimp (Whatu Ura)
Phronima novaezelandiae
Remarkable for the habit of the male of excavating the body of a
transparent jelly-like pelagic or floating sea-squirt, known as a salp, and
taking up his abode within. *Phronima* is about 30 mm long and
transparent except for its red eyes. It is a creature of the open seas, but
numbers often wash ashore after storms, particularly at St Clair, Dunedin.

179. Fish Louse (Pirinoa Ika)
Mothocya ihi
An example of another group of crustaceans, many of which have become
parasitic upon certain species of fish. The species illustrated is the one
commonly found in the mouth of the Piper. Its legs are developed as
hooks to fasten itself firmly in the fish's mouth, where it exacts its toll of
the food taken by its involuntary host. Piper taken in Auckland waters can
be heavily parasitised.

Water Fleas and Ostracods are tiny crustacea, the former common in
freshwater ponds and the latter equally common in fresh or salt water.
The ostracods are enclosed in tiny bivalved shells. Examples may be
found by washing seaweeds or pond-weed. (Not figured.)

180. Spiny Crayfish (Kōura Moana)
Jasus edwardsi
The common marine crayfish of the fish markets. It grows to about
450 mm long and occurs all around our rocky coasts, where it lives in
caverns and amongst seaweed. It is a brightly coloured species variously
marked with reddish-purple and orange. When cooked the shell of the
crayfish goes a uniform red. The species is widespread, being common
also in Chile, South Africa and southern Australia. Like crabs and other
crustaceans the crayfish grows by an extraordinary series of moults. In
this process of casting the shell, the whole of the limy jointed armour
comes off in one piece, the limbs being withdrawn as a hand is withdrawn
from a glove. For a brief time the crayfish is soft-bodied and must retire to
a safe hiding place until a new shell forms and hardens. The female
crayfish carries her eggs attached to the swimmerets under the tail. The
number of eggs carried by one female varies from 3,000 to nearly
100,000. The marine crayfish differs from a lobster in lacking pincers.

181. Smooth-tailed Crayfish (Kōura Uriuri)
Jasus verreauxi
This is not nearly so abundant in New Zealand waters as the Spiny
Crayfish and it seems to occur only in North Auckland waters and in the
Bay of Plenty. Outside New Zealand it is found at the Kermadec Islands,
New South Wales and at many localities in the Indian Ocean. It grows
much larger than *J. edwardsi* and is readily distinguished by its uniformly
dark greenish colour and smooth segments of the tail.

182. Freshwater Crayfish (Kōura)
Paranephrops planifrons
New Zealand has three species of freshwater crayfish, which should be
termed lobsters since they have powerful pincers. They are found in most
districts in small streams, lakes and ponds. These crayfish are about
125 mm long and are of dull greenish colour. Just before moulting,
crayfish form a dome-shaped body of lime in the stomach. This is a
reservoir of lime to be used in the formation of the new shell.
P. zealandicus is found in South Canterbury, Otago and Stewart Island,
P. setosus in Canterbury to as far south as Winchester, and *P. planifrons*
in the North Island and northern and western parts of the South Island.

183. *Mantis Shrimp* (Mana)
Lysiosquilla spinosa

This is 75-100 mm long, of pinkish buff colour, mottled with dark purplish-brown. It occurs throughout New Zealand and lives on sandy or muddy intertidal flats where it excavates deep burrows sometimes to a depth of 500 mm. Since the body is very flexible the animal can turn and completely reverse its position in the narrow burrow. Note the curious pincers which give a resemblance to the insect, the Praying Mantis. The pincers operate like the blade of a pocket-knife snapping into the handle.

184. *Prawn Killer* (Mōwhiwhiti)
Ibaccus alticrenatus

This is of dull salmon colour and grows about 100 mm long. It is an uncommon deep-water species found originally in 275 m off Cape Egmont, but is now known from additional specimens trawled off Cape Maria van Diemen and in the Bay of Plenty. In South Australia a related species is termed the "Prawnkiller". Note the broad shovel-shaped plates in front, which are a modification of the second pair of feelers.

185. *Large Shore Crab* (Pāpaka Nui)
Leptograpsus variegatus

The aggressive crab which scuttles away into crevices when disturbed. With back to the wall he always shows fight – claws open and raised ready to contest with any intruder. This crab is found about half tide on rocky ground, particularly on the Auckland west coast. It is mottled dull reddish-purple and white with some edging of bright violet. The legs are flattened and smooth and the back or "carapace" is approximately square with inconspicuous oblique folds at the sides. It is common in the North Island, the Kermadec Group, Australia and the islands of the South Pacific.

186. *Large Red Crab* (Pāpaka Ura)
Plagusia chabrus

This is even larger than *L. variegatus* sometimes having an overall width of 220 mm. It is more or less brick-red in colour, has sharp serrations on the edge of the carapace, ridged legs, and is partially covered with short, stiff, brownish hairs. Its movements are very fast and it will frequently attack or feign attack if one enters the water near to it. This crab is wide ranging also, for it has been recorded from Australia, South Africa, and Chile. In New Zealand it is found amongst seaweed-covered rocks at low tide, and is common in both the North and South Islands to as far south as Lyttelton.

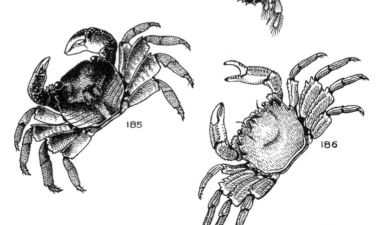

187. *Swimming Crab* (Pāpaka)
Ovalipes catharus

This is common on most exposed sandy beaches throughout New Zealand. It is at once distinguished by the broad paddle-shaped back legs which are admirably adapted for both swimming and digging in loose sand. If you disturb these crabs in shallow water they place their claws aloft in a defensive attitude and then subside quickly into the sand until only their eyes appear above the surface. Something like the gradually disappearing Cheshire Cat in *Alice in Wonderland*. They are very aggressive and will nip the soles of your feet if you stand on the sand over the spot where they lie hidden. The general colouring is speckled bluish to sandy grey with two violet-coloured blotches near the bottom of the carapace. They grow 100-150 mm in total width.

188. *Camouflaged Spider Crab* (Pāpaka Huna)
Notomithrax peronii

The slender-legged triangular-bodied crab which is rendered inconspicuous by a tangled covering of marine growth. These crabs have been observed in the act of removing living seaweeds and other marine growths with their claws and attaching these growths to hooked hair processes on the back, which are adapted for the purpose. The camouflage is so perfect that only the movement of the crab reveals its presence. Another species, the small Moss-crab *Notomithrax minor*, is usually found in rock pools.

189. *New Zealand Cancer Crab* (Ngāhorohoro)
Cancer novaezelandiae

Distinguished by its large, broadly oval back, but comparatively small legs. It is of dull reddish-brown colour and grows to 90 mm across the back, or carapace. It is very sluggish and makes little effort to escape. Common in both North and South Islands under stones at low tide.

190. *Freshwater Crab* (Pāpaka Wai Māori)
Halicarcinus lacustris

Our only freshwater crab is an insignificant species with a carapace about 10 mm across. It was found originally in Lake Pupuke, Takapuna, Auckland, but is now known from Lake Waikare, Waipa River and lagoons at Ahipara and Waikato Heads. That the change from a marine habitat is not recent is evidenced by the wide distribution of this crab, which occurs also in fresh water at Norfolk Island, Lord Howe Island and Victoria.

Small Sea Spiders (Waerau)
Halicarcinus spp.

These are tiny marine crabs of similar shape to the above. The carapace seldom exceeds 10 mm across and they are remarkable for their flatness. The carapace is sharp-edged like a coin and the middle is indented. They live among bunches of seaweed, sertularian growths on mussels and under smooth, clean stones at low tide. About 14 species are known from New Zealand. (Not figured.)

191. *Mud Crab* (Kairau)
Helice crassa

Everyone has noticed the scuttling scurrying hordes of little square-backed drab-coloured crabs so evident on all our mud-flats and in tidal creeks. They feed upon the minute particles of organic matter with which the mud is impregnated. They are quick in their movements, always ready to dart down tunnels which they construct in the mud, but in spite of their activity and wariness, fish, sea-birds, and kingfishers in particular, claim many victims. Both *Helice crassa* and a similar species, *Macrophthalmus hirtipes*, are very abundant on the mud-flat at Hobson Bay, Auckland.

Pea Crab *(Potikete)*
Pinnotheres novaezelandiae
The small soft-bodied crab found within the shell of the common edible mussel. Probably a case of commensalism – that is, the crab is not parasitic on the mussel, but merely lives in close association with it, taking a toll of the mussel's food, but no doubt making some small return by cleansing the mussel of waste matter not suited to its combined respiratory and feeding mechanism. (Not figured.)

192. Hairy Crab *(Pāpaka Huruhuru)*
Pilumnus novaezelandiae
This grows to about 50 mm in total width, is solitary in habit and not active. It occurs under stones at low tide, and is easily recognised by its dense covering of greyish or light brownish hairs.

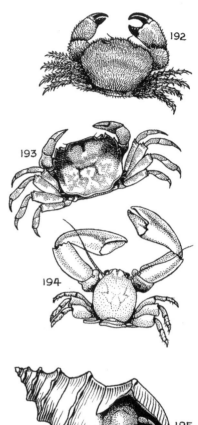

193. Common Rock Crab *(Rērere)*
Hemigrapsus edwardsi
One of the commoner intertidal New Zealand crabs, occurring on many different habitats, mud, sand, gravel, and more especially the rocky reef. When the tide is low they can be found sheltering under rocks or hiding in holes and crevices. Their usual upper surface colour is a deep purple, mottled with smallish off-white patches.

194. Half Crab *(Kawekawe)*
Petrolisthes elongatus
This is not a true crab. It has long antennae or feelers like those of the crayfish and shrimps, and the tail, although normally folded under the body, is not reduced to a narrow flap as in the true crabs (Brachyura, which means short tail). This is the small dark greenish-blue species so abundant under stones between tide marks. It is equally abundant on shelly bottom, down to 30 m, and contributes to a considerable extent to the diet of the Snapper and other bottom-feeding fish.

195. Hermit Crab *(Kāunga)*
Pagurus novaezelandiae
Like the Half Crab, this species has peculiarities which separate it from the company of the true "short tails", the Brachyura. The chief differentiating feature is the hooked abdomen which is designed to enable the Hermit Crab to occupy an empty spiral shell as a temporary refuge. As it grows, larger and larger shells have to be found for occupation. Househunting must be a complicated business for Hermit Crabs, for they have to undergo the normal crustacean moult as well. It is a queer sight to observe in a rock pool, to all intents and purposes, a slow-moving shellfish which suddenly makes off at speed – a Hermit Crab has taken possession.

196. Goose Barnacle *(Werewere)*
Lepas anatifera
This is so named on account of the fanciful medieval legend in which the Barnacle Goose was supposed to hatch out of the white shell of these stalked barnacles. The species is of world-wide distribution, being carried on driftwood and the bottoms of ships. Timber cast ashore on the Auckland west coast beaches is often completely covered with these barnacles. They are attached by a long flexible leathery stalk and the limy plates are held together by a similar leathery skin. The barnacles proper are about 35 mm long, but the stalk may extend 150-200 mm.

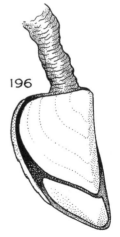

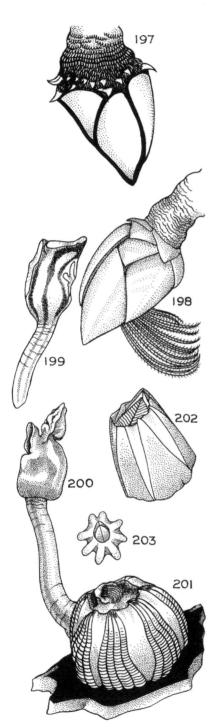

197. Stalked Barnacle (Werewere Tūkaha)
Calantica spinosa

A more rugged relative of the Goose Barnacle, varying considerably in shape due to station. It is readily distinguished, side view, by showing three large shelly plates of approximately equal size, embedded in a dark-brown leathery material. The stalk is shorter, broader and more rugged than in the previous species. It is often found in rock crevices and caverns at low water on exposed coasts. The figured example is from deeper water off Mokohinau Island.

198. Deep-sea Stalked Barnacle (Werewere Huna)
Smilium zancleanum

An uncommon species found only in deep water. The figured specimen is from the deep-sea cable off Doubtless Bay. It is distinguished from the two above species by its more numerous and differently arranged plates. Note the cirri, which are adaptations from the legs of a normal crustacean. In the barnacles the cirri are used to gather in food.

199. Striped Stalked Barnacle (Māungaunga)
Conchoderma virgatum

Occurs mostly on the bottoms of ships, but is sometimes found attached to the bodies of fish. The shelly plates are so reduced that they are scarcely apparent. The animal has a conspicuous pattern of three longitudinal brown stripes. It is of almost world-wide distribution.

200. Eared Stalked Barnacle (Māungaunga Ika Moana)
Conchoderma auritum

Related to the last species, but it is usually found attached to the body of the Humpback Whale. The Eared Stalked Barnacle is often found clustered on the Whale Barnacle, *Coronula* (described below). *Conchoderma* intercepts much food that would otherwise be gathered in by its involuntary host *Coronula*. It is soft and rather shapeless and does not show any shelly valves.

201. Whale Barnacle (Pātitotito)
Coronula diadema

This has a massive white shell, 50-70 mm in diameter. It lives exclusively attached to the Humpback Whale, where it clusters along the jaws and fins. The base of the barnacle has cavities separated by thin plates which embed firmly into the skin of the whale. *Coronula* is not truly parasitic on the whale, it merely travels along with the whale, enjoying no doubt an abundant food supply from the plankton-laden waters to which the whale migrates for its own food of larger planktonic food, the shrimp-like "whale-feed".

202. Large Pink Barnacle (Tiotio)
Balanus decorus

This grows 40 mm high and is readily recognised by the alternate white and pale pink valves of its shell. It is common cast ashore on most New Zealand coastal beaches, usually attached to large shells, but it is seldom found alive, for it lives mostly at moderate depths. It is most abundant on the Foveaux Strait oyster beds at about 25 m. Stewart Island Oysters frequently have living barnacles of this species attached to their shells.

203. Common Small Barnacle (Tio Piripiri)
Elminius modestus

The star-shaped white barnacle which clusters in thousands in the intertidal zone on anything that will afford a base of attachment. This is the pest that smothers wharf-piles and the bottoms of boats. It grows up to 10 mm in diameter and is found all around our coasts as well as Tasmania, Victoria and New South Wales. Breeding is continuous throughout the year and hence the constant need for copper-sheathing or anti-fouling paints on the bottoms of vessels.

Centipedes and Millepedes

Centipedes and millepedes are distinct from each other. Centipedes have long narrow flattened bodies divided into a large number of segments, each encased in a hard, chitinous armour. In spite of their popular name, many centipedes have considerably less than a hundred legs. Centipedes are found only on land, usually under the bark of decaying logs and beneath stones. They are carnivorous, feeding upon insects, earthworms and slugs. Each of the body segments, except the last two, has one pair of walking legs. Two of the appendages on the first body segment, are modified as poison claws, for they are perforated, allowing a poisonous secretion to be injected into their victims. Millepedes are misnamed also, for none possesses a thousand legs. They have two pairs of legs to each body segment which is round in cross section. Millepedes are herbivorous, feeding mostly on decaying vegetation and living roots. When disturbed millepedes move much more slowly than centipedes, and frequently coil themselves like a watch spring.

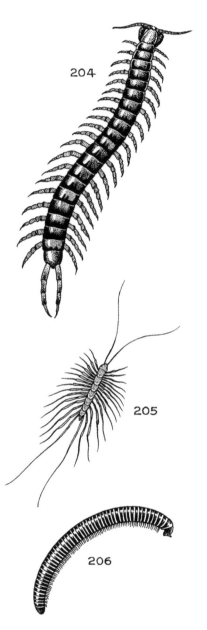

The useful qualities of the centipede as opposed to the destructive habits of the millepede are summarised in the humorous verse of Mr A.P. Herbert:

> The gardener says I ought to add,
> The centipede is not so bad;
> He rather likes the brutes.
> The millepede is what he loathes:
> He uses wild bucolic oaths,
> Because it eats his roots.
> And if you see a centipede
> Approaching with a millepede,
> Some precious root of his,
> On one of them you drop a stone,
> The other one you leave alone.

204. *Common Centipede* (Weri)
Cormocephalus rubriceps
The largest native species. It grows to over 150 mm long by 10 mm wide, and is shining dark brown to black, the paler legs often with a bluish-green tinge. This species occurs in the North Island of New Zealand, Tasmania and eastern Australia. It is particularly abundant around Auckland, where it is usually found under stones and leaves and in decaying wood.

205. *House Centipede* (Weri Waewaeroa)
Scutigera smithii
Differs from other centipedes in having long delicate legs which increase in length from the head hindwards, so that the body slopes forwards and downwards. It lives in damp places in houses and basements, but does no harm, for it feeds on cockroaches and other insects. The species is known only around Auckland, where it is common, and at Great Island, Three Kings group, where it may have been introduced with stores and equipment when the provision depot was built. It grows to about 40 mm long.

206. *Millepedes* (Weri mano)
These are very common in New Zealand, but the majority are less than 50 mm long. They are found under bark and decaying leaves, and occur both in gardens and in the forests. Their bodies are round in section and frequently alternately ringed in dark and light bands. They are sluggish and usually coil themselves into a flat spiral when disturbed.

Peripatus

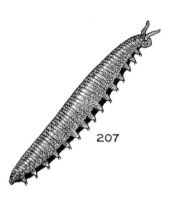

207

In spite of its small size and not very distinctive appearance, Peripatus is scientifically a most important animal, for it is a "missing link". It has some of the features of, and therefore almost bridges the gap between, two great divisions of the animal kingdom, the worms and the arthropods. Peripatus has survived in widely separated parts of the southern hemisphere, and these recent descendants have an ancestry reaching back into the distant past.

207. **Peripatus** (*Ngāokeoke*)
Peripatoides novaezealandiae
A velvety greenish or greyish-green caterpillar-like creature about 50 mm long. It has numerous stumpy legs, each fitted with pairs of curved claws and the body shows no external segmentation. Peripatus thrives only in moist situations, always away from the light. It may be found under moss and in rotten logs. It never occurs abundantly, but is not uncommon at Titirangi, near Auckland.

Insects

All joint-legged invertebrates (Arthropoda) with six legs were once placed in the Class Insecta but now are considered to be in a group called Hexapoda. The hexapods are the most abundant of all animal groups. They are classified into orders each of which has an aptly chosen name.

A few small orders are now considered not to be true insects as they have internal mouthparts and varied numbers of body segments. They have three pairs of legs attached to the thorax but are primitively wingless (have never possessed wings).

The true insects have external mouthparts, three pairs of legs attached to the thorax, and the body is divided into head, thorax and abdomen with a standard segmentation. The three pairs of legs are attached to the three thoracic segments. Wings are present on the adults in most groups and are mostly two pairs attached to the two posterior thoracic segments.

Growth is achieved by moulting the skin, and in orders with incomplete metamorphosis this goes on progressively so that young are similar in appearance to the adults, which are mature and may have wings (as in bugs). In other orders, however, there is a distinct change, known as complete metamorphosis, where the young are caterpillar – or grub-like and through an intermediate chrysalis stage become a completely different mature adult (such as moths or beetles).

The New Zealand fauna has representatives of most of the known orders of Hexapoda but not all are included here. The following orders are illustrated in this book.

Collembola (glue pegs). Primitive Hexapoda with internal mouthparts and varied numbers of body segments. Abdomen with a peg-like organ underneath and a springing apparatus under the posterior segments. Springtails.

Thysanura (tassel tails). Insects with external mouthparts. Wingless. Abdomen with three tail appendages. Silverfish.

Ephemeroptera (living-for-a-day wings). Wings reticulated by veins, hind-wings much smaller than fore-wings. Abdomen with three tail filaments. Mayflies.

Odonata (toothed). Strong mouthparts ("toothed"). Two pairs of wings each reticulated by veins. Abdomen long, straight and slender. Dragonflies, damselflies.

Blattodea (cockroaches). Flat, broad insects with long, thin antennae. Cockroaches.

Isoptera (equal wings). Social insects. Adult with two pairs of wings of equal size, longer than body and folded flat. Termites, white ants.

Mantodea (prophets). Elongate thorax, fore-legs modified for capturing prey, wings folded flat. Praying mantids.

Dermaptera (skin wings). Elongate, hard-skinned, with a pair of forceps at end of abdomen. Earwigs.

Plecoptera (plaited wings). Wings veined, fore-wings narrow, hind-wings fan-like. Abdomen with two tail filaments. Stoneflies.

Orthoptera (straight wings). Two pairs of veined wings, the fore-wings slightly thickened to form a cover for the hind-wings. Grasshoppers, locusts, wetas (wingless), crickets.

Phasmatodea (spectres). Body and legs elongate, thin. Stick insects.

Hemiptera (half wings). Fore-wings longer than hind-wings. In bugs basal part of fore-wings thickened and apical part membranous. Sucking mouthparts. Bugs, cicadas, leafhoppers, aphids, scale insects.

Megaloptera (great wings). Two pairs of large, similar, veined wings. Dobson flies.

Neuroptera (nerve wings). Two pairs of wings of similar length, with an intricate pattern of veins. Lacewings.

Coleoptera (sheath wings). Fore-wings tough opaque covers for the membranous hind-wings. Beetles, weevils.

Diptera (two wings). Fore-wings membranous, hind-wings absent or replaced by a pair of tiny balancers. Flies, mosquitoes.

Trichoptera (hair wings). Two pairs of wings covered with hairs. Caddis flies.

Lepidoptera (scale wings). Two pairs of wings clothed with tiny scales. Moths, butterflies.

Hymenoptera (membrane wings). Fore-wings longer than hind-wings, all membranous. Abdomen mostly with slender attachment to thorax. Parasitic wasps, social wasps, sawflies, bees, ants.

208. *Springtail (Tāwhana)*
Entomobrya exoricarva

This species serves to illustrate the Collembola, a group of small wingless hexapods, most of which have a forked appendage bent beneath the abdomen. This appendage is the spring, which enables these animals to leap out of harm's way when they are disturbed. Collembola are found in almost all damp situations; in leaf mould under trees, or in the forest, under bark, stones, moss, crevices of rock and even on damp sand in the inter-tidal zone. Although so small the Collembola are a vital factor in the breaking down and enrichment of soils.

208

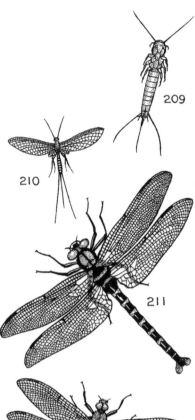

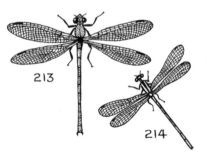

209. Silverfish (Pirirākau)
Heterolepisma zelandica

Lives under the bark of native beech trees (*Nothofagus*), but is not common. The silverfish is far better known from the introduced species which infests houses and does considerable damage by eating paper and cloth. Silverfish belong to the most primitive of the insect orders. They are entirely wingless and have never at any stage in their past history possessed wings. These insects undergo little metamorphosis, or change in form, during growth.

210. Mayfly (Piri Wai)
Atalophlebia dentata

A reddish-brown winged insect about 40 mm in total length, at once distinguished by the very small hind wings and the three conspicuous tail appendages which resemble those of the silverfish. The larvae of the mayflies live in fresh water. They have gills on the sides of the abdomen and the characteristic three tail filaments. They are either vegetarian or carnivorous, and hide under stones or in burrows in the banks of streams. Mayflies are entirely beneficial, both as larvae and as adults, for they form one of the best foods for freshwater fish. The adult mayfly has no mouthparts, so takes no food and lives for a few days only.

211. Large Dragonfly (Kapokapowai)
Uropetala carovei

This is a handsome insect with a wing spread of up to 125 mm, and a slender abdomen banded with black and yellow. These insects are rapid and agile fliers for they spend most of their time on the wing capturing small insects for food. The larva of this dragonfly lives in mud banks and swamps. It feeds on other insects above the water surface at night and takes five or six years to mature.

212. Common Dragonfly (Kapowai)
Procordulia smithii

This has a wing spread of about 80 mm and is easily distinguished by the colouring of the abdomen, which is dark in the middle but marked at the sides with broken lines of orange-brown. The head and thorax are green. Its habits are similar to those of the Large Dragonfly, but it is much more abundant. The larvae are aquatic and feed on other aquatic insects.

213. Blue Damselfly (Tīemiemi)
Austrolestes colensonis

The damselflies are smaller than the dragonflies, have a more slender abdomen, and rest with their wings in a vertical position, not outstretched. The general colour of the male Blue Damselfly is purplish-black with blue markings, but the female is black and green with white and purplish markings. These insects are often seen in summer flying near the surface of streams and ponds where the aquatic larvae occur.

214. Red Damselfly (Kihitara)
Xanthocnemis zelandica

Abundant in the vicinity of fresh water, darting about in pursuit of small insects or hovering over water. The male is bright red, but the females are black or bronze on the abdomen and yellowish on the thorax and head. Dragonflies and damselflies are wholly beneficial on account of the immense numbers of noxious insects, such as mosquitoes and sandflies, which they destroy.

215. Praying Mantis (Rō)
Orthodera ministralis

A bright grass-green insect about 40 mm long, at once distinguished by the curious front legs, which form a pair of pincers, by the first jointed section folding back on the next, very like the action of the blade snapping back into the handle of a pocket-knife. Thus the "praying" front legs are not for devotional purposes, but for "preying" upon smaller insects. It is of interest that limbs of similar form and function are found in a crustacean group – the mantis-shrimps. The egg cases (Fig. 215a) are hard brownish oblong structures about 12 mm long, commonly seen cemented to tree branches, fences or walls. This mantid is common in both New Zealand and Australia and may not be truly native here, but accidentally introduced in the early years of settlement.

216. Black Field Cricket (Pihareinga)
Teleogryllus commodus

The common shining black cricket whose cheerful high-pitched chirping is so noticeable during late summer evenings. Crickets and mantids have their "ears" in a curious place – just below the knee of the fore-limbs. Like the last species, the Black Field Cricket is common in Australia, and probably acclimatised itself here in the early colonial days. Some much smaller species are natives.

217. Spiny Stick Insect (Whē Kākāriki)
Argosarchus horridus

In spite of its formidable appearance and name, this is a harmless vegetarian. It grows to about 130 mm long, and its long slender drab-coloured body merges so perfectly with the dead twigs of a bush that only movement betrays the insect's presence.

218. Green Stick Insect (Whē Kākāriki)
Clitarchus laeviusculus

Smaller and more slender than the last species. Its bright green coloration is a perfect camouflage, for this species frequents the outer green foliage of trees and bushes. New Zealand stick insects are all wingless but elsewhere many have winged adults.

219. Black Cockroach (Pāpata)
Platyzosteria novaeseelandiae

The evil-smelling flat-backed black cockroach common throughout New Zealand. Its food consists of decaying vegetable and animal matter, and it shelters under loose stones, logs and debris. Most native cockroach species are wingless but elsewhere most are winged.

220. Mountain Grasshopper (Māwhitiwhiti)
Paprides nitidus

A small but handsome species, shining green with a yellow stripe along each side and bright red hind legs. It is found on the mountains around Lake Wakatipu. The common small dull brownish grasshopper is *Phaulacridium marginale*. The females never have wings and only about 1% of males are ever fully winged.

221. Migratory Locust (Rangataua)
Locusta migratoria

A large flying grasshopper. The term locust in New Zealand is frequently but erroneously applied to the cicada. In the Middle East and Africa closely allied species often migrate in vast swarms, leaving devastation in their wake. In summer the New Zealand species abounds on grasslands and tussock, and is easily recognised by its rapid but short and clumsy flight. It is greenish and brown with speckled fore-wings, has large powerful hind legs, and is about 50 mm long.

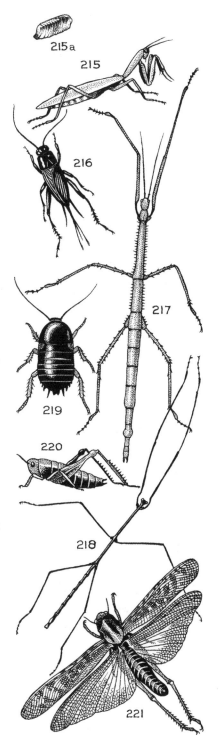

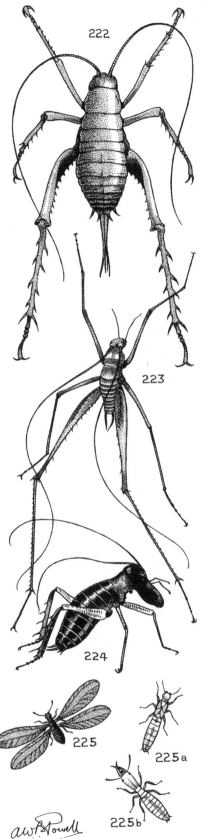

222. Giant Weta (Wētā Punga)
Deinacrida heteracantha
A large, fearsome-looking insect with a body up to 100 mm long. It is now very rare on the mainland, but still exists in fair numbers on Little Barrier Island. This weta is one of the larger species of tree wetas which feed on green leaves of trees and shrubs. They have very long slender antennae and huge hind legs, studded with sharp thorns, which can inflict a painful wound. When disturbed they kick violently and rear their hind legs almost straight upwards. The female has a stout terminal ovipositor.

223. Cave Weta (Wētā Taipo)
Gymnoplectron acanthocera
A large insect, remarkable for the extreme length of its antennae and hind legs. This species was first discovered in the Waitakere Ranges near Auckland. It has a total length of 300-350 mm, and is found on the walls of damp caves or in tree-holes in the forest. The body is small for the size of the legs, and it can be well imagined with what agility this weta leaps. The long antennae are each made up of no fewer than 550 segments.

224. Common Weta (Wētā)
Hemideina thoracica
The common tree weta, found throughout New Zealand in rotten logs, old trees, and under loose bark. At night they make a peculiar scraping sound by rubbing their hind legs against ridges on the sides of the body. The body of this species grows to about 50 mm long, and the antennae are up to 100 mm long. The male is easily recognised by the large ungainly head. Wetas are related to grasshoppers and, as they arise from winged ancestors, they are secondarily wingless.

225. Wet-wood Termite (Pōpoko Rākau)
Stolotermes ruficeps
Found in rotten logs, but another native species, *Calotermes brouni*, commonly attacks wooden houses. The native termites are small with flattened white bodies, little more than 10 mm long. The illustration shows a winged female, a worker (Fig. 225a) and a soldier (Fig. 225b). Winged adults shed their wings after a colonising flight. The allocation of duties in the termite nest is as rigid and orderly as with the ants.

226. Green Stonefly (Ngarongaro Wai)
Stenoperla prasina
The green gauzy-winged insect seen flying feebly over running water about dusk, in summer. Stoneflies differ from the mayflies in that the hind-wings greatly exceed the fore-wings in size, and stoneflies have only two tail appendages. At rest the wings lie straight back folded closely around the abdomen. The larva lives in rapidly-flowing streams, where it actively pursues its prey, which consists mainly of mayfly larvae and other small aquatic insects or their larvae.

227. Seashore Earwig (Matā)
Anisolabis littorea
This shining black insect is most frequently found under stones, logs and decaying seaweed at or near the sea coast. It does no damage for it feeds on decaying seaweed and small crustaceans. The powerful forceps of the male are always of unequal length. Forceps are used to capture prey, for offence and defence. Native earwig species are wingless but elsewhere most are winged.

228. *Large Cicada* (*Tātarakihi*)
Melampsalta cingulata

A handsome insect with a wing span of about 75 mm. The body is green with black markings and on the fore part of the head there are three red eyes like jewels, set between the two larger compound eyes. This cicada has a loud chirping song which ends with a click caused by a flick of the wings. On a hot summer's day the air seems to crackle with the volume of sound produced by hundreds of these insects singing together. Only male cicadas are capable of producing sound, and in this connection one cannot help admiring the daring of the obviously "hen-pecked" Greek poet, Xenarchus, who wrote:

> Happy are cicadas' lives,
> For they have only voiceless wives.

Cicada eggs are inserted into twigs of trees and shrubs. Larvae drop and burrow into the ground, where they extract juices from the roots of trees. When fully grown the larva becomes clothed in a horny skin and has rudimentary wings. On reaching maturity it leaves the ground, climbs up a tree trunk or post and finally the perfect insect emerges, leaving the light brown horny skin attached.

229. *Shield-bug* (*Kirirākau*)
Cermatulus nasalis

This belongs to a large group of brightly-coloured bugs noted for the triangular plate on the central part of the back. Most species of bugs suck the juices of plants and can be severe pests, but the one figured is carnivorous on caterpillars and grubs. A recently acquired habit is that it preys upon the caterpillar of the Monarch Butterfly.

230. *Planthopper* (*Kiritaitea*)
Cenchrea maorica

This species which lives on the undersides of tree fern leaves, serves to illustrate a group of small insects which feed by sucking juices from plants. There are many native species.

231. *Back-swimmer* (*Hoe Tūara*)
Anisops wakefieldi

This is the small, dark, narrow-bodied bug which swims upside down in ponds and stagnant pools. It rows itself through the water with powerful strokes of the hind pair of legs, which are flattened and fringed with hairs to increase the bearing surface. When at rest the oar-like legs project obliquely forwards. Along the underside of the abdomen there are two grooves closed over with hairs to imprison air required for breathing during submergence. Back-swimmers are carnivorous, and mosquito larvae are among their prey.

232. *Water-boatman* (*Hoehoe Tuara*)
Sigara arguta

Similar in size and in habits to the Back-swimmer, but the body is flattened dorsally instead of being narrowed laterally. It is a common insect in still fresh waters and is brown mottled all over with darker brown. Water-boatmen also devour mosquito larvae.

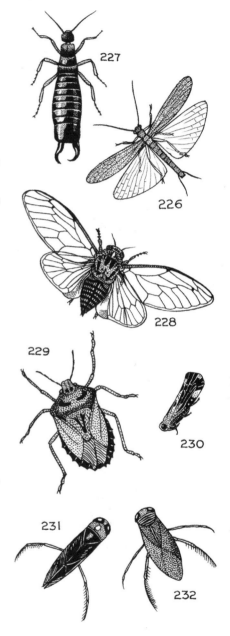

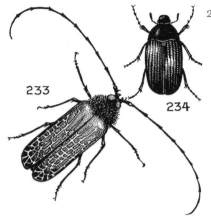

233. Huhu Beetle *(Pepe Tunga)*
Prionoplus reticularis

The largest beetle native to New Zealand. It is brownish, with an oblong body, and two long, conspicuously jointed feelers. The hard wing cases have an embossed pattern like crocodile skin. This is the large beetle that, attracted by light, enters houses during summer evenings and often causes consternation to the inmates by its noisy, clumsy flight. If incautiously handled this beetle can give a powerful nip with its large mandibles. The larva is a large fat grub known to the Māori as the "huhu" or "tunga". This grub causes considerable damage by boring tunnels into timber. Standing trees, posts, and dead trees, particularly introduced pines, are all susceptible to attack from this troublesome insect. The grub pupates in one of the tunnels it has formed in the wood, and the perfect insect emerges in the following summer. The Māori were very fond of eating the huhu grub, and it was also a favourite item of diet with the now extinct Huia.

234. Large Green Chafer *(Tanguru)*
Stethaspis suturalis

The bright shining green beetle, about 25 mm long, which often flies in considerable numbers at dusk on summer evenings. They are leaf-eaters on forest trees. The larva lives beneath the ground in forests, where it feeds on roots. It is generally observed lying on its side, curved in the form of a semi-circle. A dark yellowish-brown chafer *Costelytra zealandica*, is less than half the size of the Large Green Chafer, but the larva does considerable damage to the roots of cultivated grasses. This is the well-known Grass Grub.

235. Sand Scarab *(Mumutawa Pango)*
Pericoptus truncatus

A large, massive, shining black beetle frequently found on coastal sand dunes and beaches. The meandering tracks of these beetles are a familiar sight on the damp sand in the early morning, for they are nocturnal. The larvae are usually found in cavities in the sand under driftwood, and it is presumed that they feed largely upon decaying wood. They occur between the driftwood zone and first dune ridge and are sometimes common among roots of Marram Grass. Larvae also move about on the sand surface at night.

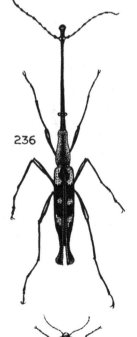

236. Giraffe Weevil *(Tūwhaipapa)*
Lasiorrhynchus barbicornis

The common name suggests a long "neck" which is actually the head extended into a proboscis. The male (illustrated) sometimes reaches a length of nearly 100 mm, but the female is always smaller. The feelers are situated near the tip of the proboscis in the male, but only half way down in the female so that it can bore into wood or bark to deposit the eggs. The larvae are active borers of a great variety of our soft-wood trees, but the perfect insect is by no means common.

237. Common Tiger Beetle *(Pāpapa)*
Neocicindella tuberculata

About 12 mm long, this is a small narrow-bodied insect of greenish colour with a cream design on its back. In summer they may be seen on dry clay banks alternately running and flying short distances in their quest for flies and other insects. The larvae are the "Penny Doctors" (Kui) of children who often endeavour to fish for them by placing straws in the long straight tunnels which are made in clay or hard earth. The larvae may be seen at times with their heads just emerging from the tunnels, ready to seize any insect that unsuspectingly comes within range.

238. *Ladybird* (*Mumutawa*)
"Scymnus" acceptus
This small ladybird beetle (3 mm long) is one of the commonest species native to New Zealand. It is recognised by a large pale yellow spot on the shoulder of each wing cover. It may be found from November to January by beating the foliage in the forest. Ladybirds are small, but they do immense good in destroying aphids and scale-insects. Commonly seen species in gardens have been introduced to combat pests.

239. *Click Beetle* (*Tūpanapana*)
Thoramus wakefieldi
Grows to more than 25 mm long, and is one of the largest of a group of insects which feign death. Click Beetles often come to rest on their backs and will suddenly right themselves by springing into the air. The springing action of the body makes a decided clicking noise. These insects are shining dark brown or black, long and narrow. The larvae of some of the numerous species of click beetles found in New Zealand are the "wire-worms" which do considerable damage to the roots of plants.

240. *Ground Beetle* (*Kurikuri*)
Megadromus vigil
A handsome bluish-black, slender-waisted beetle with deep longitudinal striations on the wing covers. It is one of the most abundant ground beetles in the Wellington district, where it occurs under stones and logs in damp situations. This species is just under 25 mm long, but another, *Plocamostethus planiusculus*, is slightly larger and even more abundant. They are ferocious predators, and will nip the human skin with their powerful mandibles, unless handled carefully. The larva is about 30 mm long and is found under large logs where there is dry soil beneath.

241. *Striped Longhorn* (*Mumu Poka*)
Navomorpha sulcata
A native wood-boring beetle. The adult insect is under 12 mm long, narrow-bodied and tapering behind. It is dark-brown with a greenish sheen, while down each side is a broad greyish split stripe with a forked one in the middle. The female bores small holes in bark and deposits her eggs, which on hatching develop into white cylindrical larvae with broad heads. The larvae eventually bore deeply into the heart wood. Other well-known longhorn or "longicorn" borers are the Lemon Tree Borer, *Oemona hirta*, the Variegated Longhorn, *Coptomma variegatum*, and the Two-toothed Longhorn, *Ambeodontus tristis*, which does considerable damage to wooden buildings.

242. *False Wireworm Beetle* (*Mumu Popo*)
Mimopeus opaculus
A flat dull beetle commonly found in and under logs which are in an advanced state of decay. The larva, one of the "false wireworms" is nearly 50 mm long, very highly polished and deep yellowish-brown.

243. *Crane Fly* (*Matua Waeroa Rere*)
Holorusia novarae
Sometimes called "Daddy-long-legs" (but see 279). One of the largest of some 500 species known in New Zealand. This one, which has a narrow body about 25 mm long, but with a leg spread of over 75 mm, is found around Auckland in great numbers during spring and summer. The wings are smoky-grey, veined and marked in brown. Another common species, *Macromastix albistigma*, is pale green. Our most attractive species, *M. ferrugosa*, is bright orange and black. The crane fly larvae live in damp ground, decaying wood, and especially in the marshy banks of streams and swamps.

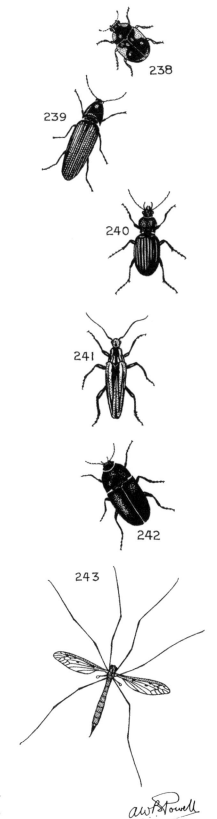

244. *Vigilant Mosquito* (Wāeroa)
Culex pervigilans

One of three species of mosquitoes common in and around Auckland city. It is the usual intruder of dwellings, whose high-pitched buzzing and irritating bite disturbs one's slumbers. The larvae are the common "wrigglers" which infest all stagnant water. Old tins and bottles littered in untidy properties, and rubbish dumps especially, act as excellent nurseries for this little pest. Any container that collects rain water, however small, assists the breeding of this species. Subject to favourable temperatures this mosquito will breed all through the year. Another local mosquito, *Aedes notoscriptus*, is a silent flier and a daytime biter. Its favourite habit is to quietly settle and bite the legs rather than the hands or face. It operates mostly in the early morning and late afternoon, or all day during dull weather. The larvae of *A. notoscriptus* favour water containers that are well sheltered from the bright light, and are able to remain submerged for a longer period than those of *C. pervigilans*, which frequently wriggle to the surface to breathe.

245. *New Zealand Glow Worm* (Titiwai)
Arachnocampa luminosa

Few countries can boast of a tourist attraction based upon a two-winged fly. The Waitomo Caves in New Zealand and a similar cave in New South Wales are world famous for the brilliant phosphorescent spectacle caused by the presence of huge colonies of the larvae of one of the fungus gnats. The figured adult is a male of rather similar shape to a crane fly, but it has a long slender abdomen just under 12 mm long which is alternately banded in light and dark brown. The wings are smoky-grey veined in dark brown. Glow Worms in New Zealand are not confined to the Waitomo Caves, but may be seen on dark nights under shaded damp banks in most areas of native forest. The larva spins a small web in front of its burrow and later the pupa is suspended from this web. The phosphorescent light is emitted from the rear end of the body.

246. *Hover-fly* (Ngaro Paira)
Helophilus trilineatus

A handsome fly about 20 mm long and brightly coloured – the thorax is grey with three vertical broad bands of black and the abdomen is velvety black with a golden rectangular patch on each side of the top segment. This is the fly of the countryside which alternately hovers and darts off at speed. Larvae inhabit putrid waters and are known as "rat-tailed maggots" from the long telescopic breathing tube at the rear end. Adult hover-flies feed on the nectar of flowers, and the larvae of some species are beneficial in destroying aphids and other plant pests.

247. *New Zealand Blue Blow Fly* (Ngaro Iro)
Calliphora quadrimaculata

The common blow fly, found throughout New Zealand from the shore to the snow line. It is about 12 mm long, has a black thorax and violet-blue abdomen. The larvae feed on dung, decaying seaweed, and any putrefying matter. This fly is a great pest for it "blows" meat, woollen materials and especially blankets if they are hung out in the sunlight.

248. *Black Hunting Wasp* (Ngaro Wīwī)
Salius monachus

A handsome shining black wasp with a wing span of 40 mm. The wings are iridescent coppery. Better known wasps are the "mud-daubers" or so-called "mason-bees" which block up keyholes and construct clay compartments in odd corners of houses. These structures are used to imprison small spiders, which are stung and rendered torpid by the wasp and ultimately serve as food for the larvae, for an egg is laid in each compartment. Wasps are distinguished from bees by their slender waists and general absence of hairs on the body.

249. *Giant Rhyssa* (*Ngaro Whiore*)
Certonotus fractinervis

A rare species of "ichneumon", or long-tailed wasp, which is found mostly in the western rain forests of the South Island. It is a handsome black and yellow insect with pale gold iridescent wings. The body is 40 mm long and the ovipositor, trailing behind, is 70 mm long. The larvae of the ichneumons are all parasitic on caterpillars and the larvae of saw-flies and wood-boring beetles. The extremely long ovipositor is for probing into wood and soil to reach and infest the larvae with eggs.

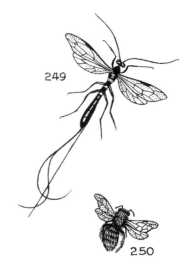

249

250. *Solitary Bee* (*Ngaro Huruhuru*)
Paracolletes fulvescens

All species of native bee are smaller than the introduced Honey Bee and are noted for their extremely hairy pollen-carrying hind legs. They are mostly dark grey with golden-brown hairs. These bees burrow in the ground, especially in clay and are solitary in the sense that each builds its own nest and gathers its own supply of honey.

250

251. *Ant* (*Pōpokorua*)
Monomorium antarcticum

This species is nearly 10 mm long and is golden brown with three black bands on the abdomen. Volumes have been written on the social habits of ants, for their ways are even more complex than those of the bees. The fact that an ant colony is the offspring of more than one female makes for its greater permanency, for where only one female is present, as with the bees, an accident may bring disaster to the whole community. Only males and females are winged – the males die in this condition, but the females return to the nest and cast their wings before commencing egg-laying. The neuters, ordinary workers and soldiers, are permanently wingless and have the thorax very narrow. Their daily routine consists not only of keeping the nest clean, gathering food, and feeding the larvae, but also the carrying of eggs to those parts of the nest where they will obtain the greatest warmth. This involves moving them to within the influence of the sun's warmth during the day and again to the depths of the nest for the night. The oblong white objects which ants are seen moving about with such determination are the cocoons containing the pupae. Most native ants are to be found under stones and logs in open country or in the forests. The chief invaders of houses are introduced species.

251

252. *Dobson Fly* (*Ngaro Parirau*)
Archichauliodes diversus

The Dobson Fly has four large wings expanding up to 80 mm, which are curved over the body when at rest. They are tinted with brown, particularly the forewings. The larva (Fig. 252a) is the common Toe-biter found in streams. It has a dark head and thorax and menacing jaws always open ready for their prey which consists of other aquatic insects. There are obvious filaments on the side of each abdominal segment, and a pair of hooked prolegs at the tail which help to hold the larva in position in running water.

252

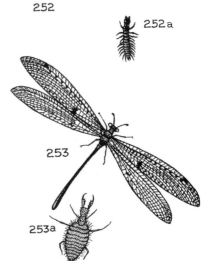

252a

253. *Ant-lion Lacewing* (*Kutukutu*)
Weeleus acutus

This insect has four long wings with a span of about 90 mm, but a slow flight. The clear wings with many veins and cross-veins give a lacy effect and the veining is blotched with brown in places. At rest the wings are folded back, roof-like over the body. The larva of this lacewing is the extraordinary Ant-lion (Fig. 253a) which constructs little craters in sand or dust. At the bottom of the crater the Ant-lion lies buried, all except its powerful jaws, which immediately grab unsuspecting ants as they slither down the loose sides of the crater. The adult lacewing is seldom seen on the wing as it is nocturnal but occasionally enters houses, being attracted by bright lights.

253

253a

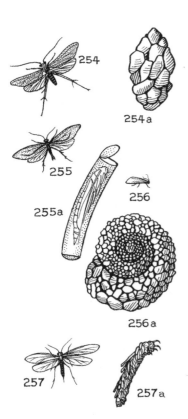

254. *Common Net-building Caddis Fly* (Ngaro Waiwai)
Hydropsyche colonica

Caddis flies are insignificant insects with four wings clothed in fine hairs and with extra-long hind-legs. At rest the wings lie roof-like over the abdomen. In this species wings are light brown and span about 25 mm. Eggs of caddis flies are laid in a gelatinous mass under water, and the early stages are entirely aquatic. In this species the aquatic larva constructs a net between stones for catching food but later builds a strong cover (Fig. 254a) in which it changes into the chrysalis. Caddis flies are beneficial, both as larvae and as adults, for they contribute to the diet of freshwater fish, birds, lizards, frogs and dragonflies.

255. *Horny-cased Caddis Fly* (Ngaro Pū)
Olinga feredayi

Fore-wings of the adult caddis fly are yellowish-brown and in the male there is a noticeable thin strip of thicker hairs parallel to the posterior and distal margins. The larva forms a slightly-curved tubular case of light-brown horny material (Fig. 255a), which it caps at both ends before changing to a chrysalis. The front-end cap is pushed open when the adult is ready to emerge under water.

256. *Spiral Caddis Fly* (Ngaro Tōrino)
Helicopsyche albescens

This is a small pale caddis fly with a wing span of about 9 mm. The larval case (Fig. 256a) is spiral like a small snail shell and is covered with minute sand grains.

257. *Marine Caddis Fly* (Ngaro Waitai)
Philanisus plebejus

An unusual caddis fly which inhabits the rocky sea-shore. It is pale with a wing span up to 20 mm. The female has a short stiff ovipositor and lays eggs into starfish. The larva builds a case of *Corallina* seaweed (Fig. 257a) in the sea below low water or in rock pools.

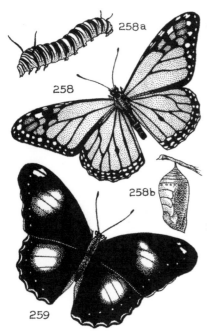

258. *Monarch Butterfly* (Kahukū)
Danaus plexippus

A handsome orange-coloured butterfly, conspicuously veined and patterned in black, and with a wing span of 80-100 mm. The male has a black scent organ on a vein near the centre of each hind-wing. The caterpillar (Fig. 258a) is conspicuously ringed with cream and black, and has a pair of soft wavy filaments at each end of the body. The chrysalis (Fig. 258b) is a pale jade casket with a circle of gold-like specks near the top. The Monarch Butterfly is a North American species which has vastly increased its distribution during the past 150 years. At first it was a vagrant to New Zealand but is now established here so long as suitable food plants for the caterpillars are grown. Females lay eggs on milk-weed plants (*Asclepias*, which includes the Swan Plant), and these are natural food plants. Caterpillars can also survive if fed on Moth-catching Plant (*Araujia*).

259. *Blue Moon Butterfly* (Kahupōuri)
Hypolimnas bolina nerina

A great rarity in New Zealand, where it occurs from time to time as a vagrant, probably from Australia, where it is common. The male (figured) is velvety black with a rounded white spot edged with electric-blue, one on each of its four wings. The slightly larger female has a wing span of 100 mm and includes patterns in orange and cream additional to a general coloration as in the male. So far neither the eggs nor the caterpillar of this species have been found in New Zealand.

260. *Yellow Admiral Butterfly* (*Kahukōwhai*)
Bassaris itea

A common butterfly with a wing expansion of up to 65 mm, seen from November until May. The fore-wings are black and reddish-brown, divided by a broad diagonal patch of yellow. The hind-wings are black and reddish-brown, having four black circles with blue centres on the lower part of each wing. The food plant of the caterpillar is the Common Stinging Nettle. Beyond New Zealand the species is found throughout Australia, Tasmania and the Loyalty Islands.

261. *Red Admiral Butterfly* (*Kahukura*)
Bassaris gonerilla

This is about the same size as the Yellow Admiral and like it the caterpillar feeds on nettles. The butterfly is black with conspicuous transverse bars of red on each wing. Those of the hind-wings each bear four black rings with blue centres. This native species is generally distributed in New Zealand and appears from January to April. The two species of *Bassaris* are strong fliers, and are very wary and hard to catch.

262. *Australian Painted Lady Butterfly* (*Pēpē Parahua*)
Cynthia kershawi

As the popular name suggests, this is a brightly-coloured butterfly of 50-65 mm wing span. The upper portions of the wings are black with white markings and the lower portions orange, distinctively patterned in black. Near the lower edge of the hind-wings are a series of black rings with blue centres. This species is a well-known migrant, for it makes its way to practically all parts of the world, sometimes moving in vast swarms. In New Zealand it has been recorded from most districts, but it seldom occurs abundantly, and its numbers appear to fluctuate greatly from season to season. It is usually seen from January to April.

263. *Common Blue Butterfly* (*Pēpē Aouri*)
Zizinia otis

This is about 25 mm across with pale blue wings bordered with dull brown. It is seen abundantly on dry grassland and sand dunes during summer.

264. *Common Copper Butterfly* (*Pēpē Parariki*)
Lycaena salustius

This has a span of up to 40 mm and the wings are bright coppery orange, bordered and veined in black. It is seen from November to April and is most abundant on tussock grasslands and amongst low scrub.

265. *Black Mountain Ringlet Butterfly* (*Pēpē Pouri*)
Percnodaimon pluto

This is restricted to the tops of the mountain ranges of the South Island. It has a wing span of up to 50 mm and is bronzy black except for a pale patch at the outer extremity of each fore-wing, upon which there are four or five small black rings with white centres. The species frequents shingle screes at 1,200-1,800 m and the caterpillar most probably feeds on the Carpet Grass *Poa colensoi*.

266. *Magpie Moth* (*Pūrere Uri*)
Nyctemera annulata

The black and white day-flying moth so abundant throughout New Zealand. The caterpillar is black and red, covered with numerous tufts of black hair, it is the well-known "Woolly-bear" commonly found feeding on the leaves of many plants of the daisy family, particularly Groundsel and Cineraria. The caterpillars, when about to pupate, attach themselves by a silk casing to a tree trunk or any suitable object. In four to six weeks the perfect insect emerges. The season for the regular appearance of the moth is September to April.

267. Peacock Moths (Pūrere Parangunu)
Dasypodia cymatoides, D. selenophora

Handsome moths up to 75 mm in wing span, which are frequently found quietly resting on the walls or ceilings in houses during February, March and April. They are dark velvety-brown, with darker zigzag markings, and two conspicuous bluish crescents on the fore-wings. The caterpillar is over 50 mm long, cylindrical, and dull yellowish brown thickly speckled with black. They feed on the leaves of wattle.

268. North Island Lichen Moth (Pūrerehua)
Declana atronivea

A very handsome species restricted to the North Island. It has a wing span of up to 50 mm and is at once distinguished by the black and white patterned fore-wings and grey hind-wings. The apparently startling contrast of colour in this moth is actually distinctly protective when the insect is in its natural setting. The vigorous black markings tend to confuse the outline of the insect in the same way as bold camouflage on military ships and vehicles proves effective.

269. Cabbage Tree Moth (Pūrere Ti)
Epiphryne verriculata

Another fine example of protective resemblance. The moth always rests lengthwise on the dead leaves of the Cabbage Tree, so that the brown lines on the insect's wings merge with the parallel veins of the leaf. Also the ground colour of the moth is light brownish, of similar colour to that of the dead leaf. The caterpillar feeds on the green leaves of the Cabbage Tree. The moth has a wing span of 40 mm, is generally distributed in New Zealand, and is seen from October until May.

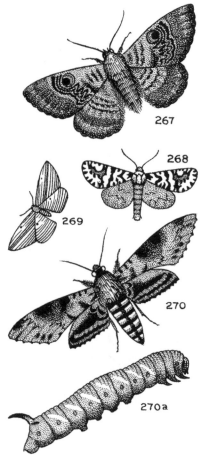

267

268

269

270

270a

270. Sphinx Moth (Hihue)
Herse convolvuli

This handsome, widely distributed moth is of almost world-wide occurrence. In New Zealand it is most abundant in the Nelson and Auckland districts. The wing span is about 90 mm and it is greyish, marked and speckled with dark brown. The abdomen is ringed with black, red and white, and has a vertical dark median stripe. The caterpillar (Anuhe, Fig. 270a) reaches 80-90 mm long, is either green or brownish, and has at the rear end a large backwardly curved spine like a rose-thorn. It feeds on any of the several species of convolvulus, particularly the pink and white one common near the sea shore. It is also found at times feeding on Kumara leaves. The caterpillar buries itself in the ground in February to pupate, but does not emerge as a perfect insect until November or December.

271. Plume Moth (Pūrerehuru)
Alucita furcatalis

A delicate little moth with a wing expansion of less than 25 mm. It rests with its narrow forked fore-wings rigidly outstretched and looks just like a tiny aeroplane. The hind-wings are divided into delicate plume-like processes. The figured species is found in most parts of New Zealand in dense forest, but it and allied species are not uncommon in gardens and houses during summer.

272. Bag Moth (Pū A Raukatauri)
Liothula omnivora

This is best known by its tapering, conical, brownish case of silk, strengthened with bits of leaves and twigs, which is commonly found suspended from the limbs of trees, particularly Manuka and Macrocarpa. The male Bag Moth is an inconspicuous, dark brownish, swift-flying moth, but the female is without wings, legs and antennae, for it remains in the case to produce and tend to the eggs.

273. **Puriri Moth** (*Pepetuna*)
Aenetus virescens

This is the largest of our native moths, and it is confined to the North Island of New Zealand. The male Puriri Moth has bright green fore-wings with various paler markings, the hind-wings are yellowish brown near the body, but merge into white and finally green at the edges. In the female the fore-wings are green, mottled with black, and the hind-wings reddish-brown to green. The wing expansion of the male is 100 mm, but the female sometimes spans up to 150 mm. The caterpillar bores a large 7-shaped tunnel in the outer heartwood of a number of native trees such as Puriri, Wineberry, *Hoheria* and Manuka. In cultivated surroundings it has been known to attack willows, oaks and apple trees. The eggs are produced in large numbers, and scattered at random by the flying female. They resemble small round smooth shot, and are yellowish at first, but later turn black. The perfect insect emerges from October onwards, and although they are seldom seen in their natural surroundings a certain number find their way into houses or the vicinity of street lights, for, like most moths, they are attracted to bright lights.

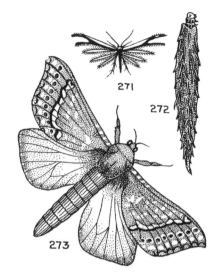

Spiders

Spiders are easily distinguished from insects by having eight legs instead of six and only two body divisions, the cephalothorax (head and thorax combined), and the abdomen, which is usually soft and unsegmented. They lack the compound eyes of insects, but have as a rule either six or eight simple eyes. Underneath at the front, spiders have powerful fangs, used to hold their prey, which is then paralysed by the injection of a toxic fluid. The webs which spiders construct are produced from a sticky substance extruded from the spinnerets at the terminal end of the abdomen. The silken threads so produced often span considerable distances between trees, for the spider takes advantage of wind and produces a long slender thread initially which drifts across the gap. The web is so sticky that insect victims are easily snared by it. Newly-hatched spiders resemble their parents and grow by casting their skins five to six times. They do not undergo the elaborate metamorphosis of many insects. A general name for spiders in New Zealand is pūngāwerewere. General names for the cobweb are whare pūngāwerewere and tukutuku.

274. **Nursery Spider** (*Tuarahonu*)
Dolomedes minor

The large active spider of the fields, gardens and swamps. It is best known by its gauze-like nests which envelop the outer twigs of bushes. This spider is brownish with pinkish grey and black vertical streaks on the cephalothorax. The legs are thick at the body but taper rather rapidly, and the span is approximately 50 mm. Other species of *Dolomedes* are the water-spiders, which are capable of entering either fresh or salt water, but require a partially immersed object to crawl down to exert sufficient leverage to break the surface film. Some of these spiders span up to 75 mm. They have been known to kill small fish.

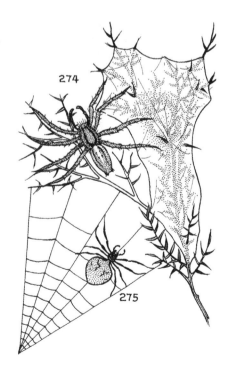

275. **Orb Web Spider** (*Pūngā Matamatakupenga*)
Aranea pustulosa

This orb web spider has small slender legs with a broad and inflated soft abdomen which bears five small knobs at the tip. Orb web spiders are very abundant and produce the elaborate geometric webs which are objects of great beauty, particularly when they are heavily covered with dew in the early morning.

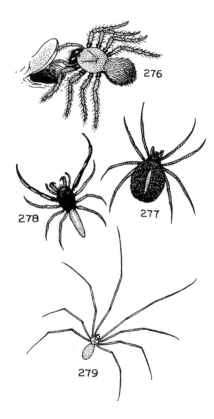

276. *Trapdoor Spider* (Pūngākarirua)
Cantuaria gilliesi

A heavily built dark-brown spider with thick hairy legs, and a span of nearly 50 mm. It has a very characteristic dent in the smooth cephalothorax, and the abdomen is oval, thickly set with fine hairs. The Trapdoor and related spiders have powerful fangs which work up and down instead of sideways as in other spiders. The nest of *C. gilliesi* is neatly constructed, consisting of a tubular tunnel in the ground about 25 mm in diameter, lined with silk, and closed at ground level with a tightly fitting, circular hinged lid made of the same material.

277. *Katipo Spider* (Katipō)
Latrodectus katipo

This is neither large nor common, but it is dreaded because of its venomous bite. This spider is little more than 25 mm in span and is characterised chiefly by its large globular abdomen; often with an orange or red stripe down the middle. The Katipo occurs northwards of Banks Peninsula, but its distribution appears haphazard. It is most often seen under driftwood on coastal sand dunes.

278. *Jumping Spider* (Tūpekepeke)
Trite bimaculosa

An active little spider less than 25 mm long, easily recognised by its large powerful fore-limbs and small narrowly cylindrical light-coloured abdomen. It runs at considerable speed, darting over the ground in search of insect prey. This spider does not construct a web for ensnaring its prey, but actively hunts small insects.

279. *Daddy-long-legs Spider* (Matua Waeroa)
Pholcus phalangioides

This is most abundant in outbuildings and also in houses if cleaning is neglected for more than a few days. It is easily recognised by its extremely long and slender light-coloured legs and ridiculously small soft body. The web is rather untidy and usually bridges a corner of a ceiling or the eaves of houses. It is a cosmopolitan species, very common around Auckland, and possibly introduced.

Tunicates (Sea-squirts)

The sea-squirts are those dull, uninteresting leathery growths on rocks or wharf piles that suddenly eject a narrow jet of water. Their shapelessness masks a relatively high organisation, for structurally they are chordates, the group to which the vertebrates belong. They are descendants of an early offshoot from the ancestral stock that gave rise to the backboned animals. The larval sea-squirt is a free-swimming creature with a tail and semblance of a notochord, the forerunner of the backbone. After a short time, however, the larva attaches itself to some stationary object, the tail and notochord disappear, and it grows about itself the tough leathery tunic to which the name tunicate alludes. In its adult form the tunicate's body is largely occupied by a complex sieve-like system of gills. The two openings in the tunic allow a continuous passage of sea water from which organic particles are extracted by the animal. The two diagrams below Fig. 284 show respectively, larval tunicates and a section through an adult.

280. Barrel Salp (Kāeo Riki)
Doliolum sp.
One of a large group of pelagic or drifting open-sea tunicates which are referred to as salps. The tunic is transparent and jelly-like and they are almost invisible in the water. The Barrel Salp is about 35 mm long and is notable as the victim of the Barrel-shrimp (see under crustaceans) which eats out the interior of the salp and takes up its abode within.

281. Fire Salp (Kāeo Hineatore)
Pyrosoma sp.
This is really a large colony of tunicates living attached to the outside of a semi-transparent hollow cylinder. They are pelagic denizens of the open sea and at night are remarkable for their fiery phosphorescence. The figured example is about 100 mm long and was taken in Cook Strait. Some species attain a length of 1.2 m.

282. Sea Tulip (Kāeo)
Boltenia pachydermatina
A tunicate with a long stalk attachment. They are found in numbers amongst seaweeds at low tide in the South Island, and especially at the Chatham Islands. The stalks grow 150-250 mm long and the body proper up to 75 mm. They are buff coloured, mottled with reddish-purple.

283. Kāeo kura
Microcosmus kura
A warty, dirty-white to brownish tunicate common in Auckland waters, where it occurs attached to stones, old shells and seaweeds.

284. A smooth tunicate of the family Styelidae
They are about 50 mm long and are found attached to the undersides of stones at low tide, in crevices, and often inside old bivalve shells. One, Kāeo Piringa *Asterocarpa coerulea*, is bluish, and others are pink or red.

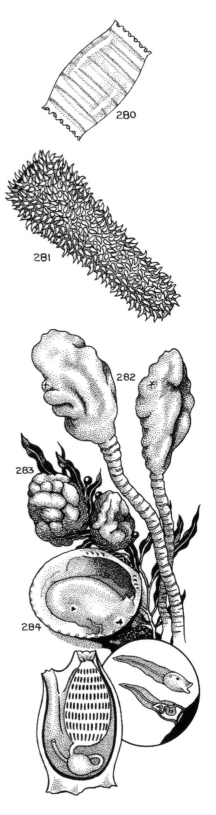

Fish and Fish-like Animals

Fish-like animals have an ancestry that pre-dates all other vertebrates. True fish, like the Snapper, have a well-developed bony skeleton in common with frogs, lizards, birds and mammals. The lampreys and the sharks, together with the more primitive sea-squirts and Amphioxus, bridge the evolutionary gap between the soft-bodied invertebrates and the vertebrates. Amphioxus has no head, and a gelatinous rod of tissue, the "notochord", instead of a skeleton. The lamprey has a head, but no lower jaw, and still the "notochord", not a backbone. The sharks and rays have backbones but they are composed of cartilage, not bone.

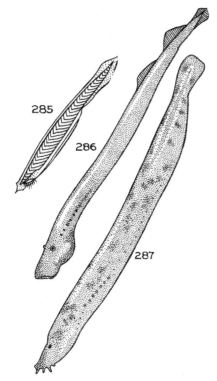

285. **Amphioxus** *(Puhi)*
Zeamphioxus hectori
A small leaf-life semi-transparent creature of about 50 mm total length. It has no head, limbs or paired fins, and no backbone, just an unjointed rod of gelatinous tissue, termed the "notochord". Though it can swim freely it is mostly a burrowing animal, living in clean sand just off coastal beaches. Amphioxus, sometimes called Lancelet, retains the habit of ciliary feeding, probably akin to that of the earliest ancestors of the chordates.

286. **Lamprey** *(Piharau)*
Geotria australis
Lampreys differ from the true fish in the total absence of paired fins, jaws and other bony structures; the backbone is represented by its primitive forerunner, the "notochord". The mouth is a roundish sucker having a series of rasping teeth, with sharper and stronger ones on the tongue. There are no scales and the skin is slimy. In habits the Lamprey is as unpleasant as its appearance, for it is predaceous upon other fish. It fastens its disc-shaped mouth to the victim and rasps away the flesh. It does not eat the tissue, but confines its efforts to extracting blood and juices. Lampreys spend part of their lives in fresh water (rivers and streams), and part in the sea. The eggs are laid far up the rivers, but during its growth the young Lamprey descends the river by easy stages and is almost of adult size upon reaching the sea. In the next stage the Lamprey spends a certain time in the sea, taking on a new appearance, with a bright silvery and blue coloration. As the breeding season approaches the now adult Lampreys, about 450 mm long, ascend the rivers, gradually losing their bright colours and resolving into a dirty brown. Māori esteemed the Lamprey as food and formerly captured large numbers of them during the seasonal migration or "runs", which normally occur at night. The old-time Māori were expert at predicting the exact times for these runs.

287. **Hagfish** *(Tūere)*
Eptatretus cirrhatus
A primitive eel-like fish, closely related to the Lamprey in structure and behaviour but it lives only in marine habitats. Hagfish occur throughout the New Zealand region, from shallow water to depths of about 1,000 m, but are more common in cooler southern areas. Though blind, Hagfish are predators and scavengers of other fish, which they detect by movement and smell.

Sharks and Rays

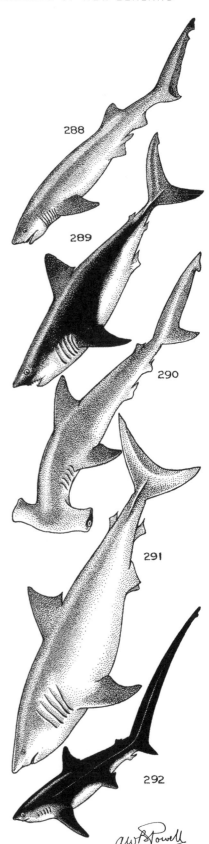

288. Seven-gilled Shark (Tuatini)
Notorhynchus cepedianus
One of three wide ranging primitive sharks distinguished by having six or seven gill slits and a single dorsal (upper) fin. This species has a broadly rounded snout and is the largest, reaching over 2 m long. It can also be recognised by colour being pale grey-brown above with scattered black or white spots, and cream white below. The teeth are distinctive and differ in each jaw; the upper ones are more or less single pointed, but the lower ones have eight or nine cusps and resemble short sections of a hacksaw blade.

289. Makō
Isurus oxyrinchus
A well-known "big-game" fish common in North Auckland waters. The species occurs also in Tasmania, Victoria, South Australia and New South Wales, where it is known as the Blue Pointer or Snapper Shark. This shark is electric blue above and white below, with a pointed snout and sharp awl-like teeth. It preys on Kahawai and other fish, and is according to anglers the only shark that takes a fast-moving bait. The Māori prize the teeth of the Makō as ear ornaments.

290. Hammerhead Shark (Mangō Pare)
Sphyrna zygaena
This shark is well named, for the lateral extensions of the skull are shaped just like a double-headed hammer. It grows up to about 3 m long, but most examples seen locally are only half that length. The colour is ashy-grey above fading to pale yellowish below. The dull bluish and brown eyes are at the extremities of the hammerhead. In Australia this shark is regarded as dangerous, since large examples frequent bathing beaches.

291. White Shark (Mangō Tuatini)
Carcharodon carcharias
A large heavy-bodied shark that can grow to 5 m long or more, found in temperate and tropical waters of all oceans. This species is the main villain, both in legend and fact, behind the shark's reputation for voracity and the ensuing human reaction of fear and repugnance. While many exaggerated tales exist about the great White Shark there are no doubts about its large appetite. A 420 kg example caught off Whangaroa had in its stomach a 1.25 m Makō, the backbone of another, an 18 kg Hapuku, a Gannet, an 11 kg lump of whale blubber and seven strands of whalebone. Apart from size, its teeth, broadly triangular with serrate edges, present an awesome picture.

292. Thresher Shark (Mangō Ripi)
Alopias superciliosus
A widespread warm-water shark easily recognised by the extremely large upper fluke of the tail, which is as long as the combined length of the head and body. The colour of the Thresher is dark bluish grey above and white below. The mouth and teeth of this shark are small, but it uses its long tail to beat the water and round up small fish upon which it feeds. The Thresher is common in North Auckland waters and is a popular game fish.

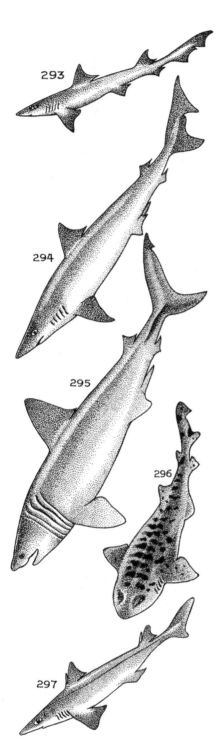

293. Spotted Smooth-hound *(Pioke)*
Mustelus lenticulatus
A very common small shark (average size 0.5-1.0 m) also known as Gummy Shark, Rig, or often sold as Lemonfish, and used in the fish and chip trade because of its boneless flesh. It is easily recognised by its colour, ashy-grey with lighter spots on the back, and small blunt teeth, arranged like a pavement, which render it inoffensive to man. The Māori of old relished the sun-dried flesh of this and other small sharks. At night this shark comes into very shallow water in search of food and is frequently encountered on the shallow flats of Auckland Harbour.

294. School Shark *(Tope)*
Galeorhinus australis
The commonest of all sharks in New Zealand waters. This is very similar in shape to the Spotted Smooth-hound, having a double-tail and pointed nose, but it has proportionately a greater girth and is much larger, attaining a length of 2.0-2.5 m. In colour it is slaty-purple to brownish above and much lighter below. The teeth are sharply pointed and serrated, but this shark is harmless to man. A closely allied American species, the Soup-fin Shark, is valued for its liver oil, and the fins, which are used as a delicacy in the preparation of the famous shark's-fin soup.

295. Basking Shark *(Reremai)*
Cetorhinus maximus
Our largest shark, but it is quite harmless, for its teeth are blunt and only 6 mm long. Its food consists of small fish and crustaceans. This shark attains a length of over 9 m, and it is purplish-brown above and greyish underneath. The most conspicuous feature is the extremely long gill slits which almost sever the head from the body. The gills are provided with comb-like processes, which the fish uses as a strainer when swallowing quantities of small crustaceans. Basking Sharks spend much of their time near the surface, and scattered loose schools can be found throughout temperate oceanic waters.

296. Carpet Shark *(Pekapeka)*
Cephaloscyllium isabella
This is a small, harmless species, about 1 m long, which frequents the sea bed, where it feeds on crabs, worms and other marine organisms. It is brown, mottled and spotted with darker brown. The body is flattened dorsally and the tail resembles that of a Spotted Smooth-hound. In shape the Carpet Shark somewhat approaches the spreading form of a Sting Ray. It is rather sluggish and prefers the deeper waters, but is commonly caught in trawls and craypots.

297. Grey Spiny Dogfish *(Pekepeke)*
Squalus blainvillei
One of a large family of spiny dogfish, most having world-wide distributions. They are identified by a sharp spine in front of each dorsal (upper) fin, and the anal fin is absent. All are bottom dwellers, many in deeper waters (500-1,000 m). This species is uniformly grey in colour and predominates in warmer northern coastal waters feeding on small fish, squid, and crabs. South of the Cook Strait region it is replaced by another species, *Squalus acanthias* (not illustrated), grey-brown with large white spots, that prefers cooler habitats.

298. Eagle Ray *(Whai Manu)*
Myliobatis tenuicaudatus

This grows to about 900 mm wide and has a thick body with a bluntly rounded snout, but the flukes are extended laterally to tapered points, so that the whole outline resembles a kite. The colour varies from dirty greenish grey to almost black. It is harmless except for a hard bony spine set at an angle on the smooth, whip-like tail. This spine can inflict a nasty wound, and is dangerous since there are poison glands and ducts associated with it. The Eagle Ray feeds largely on shellfish, which it crushes with powerful jaws lined with hexagonal flat teeth set like paving stones. This fish is common in northern waters, especially in the Hauraki Gulf, where they are frequently seen in shallow water during summer. The flesh of this ray is edible and quite palatable if soaked in fresh water for some hours to dispel a slight ammonia flavour.

299. Short-tailed Stingray *(Oru)*
Dasyatis brevicaudatus

Our largest stingray species, growing to a diameter of 2 m and a length of 4 m. It is found in southern Australia, Tasmania and New Zealand, more commonly in the North Island. This ray is sandy to greyish in colour, and apart from its large size is easily recognised by rows of spines on the tail, which resemble rose thorns, and the hard bony sting up to 200 mm long which projects at an angle about half way down the tail. A similar species, *Dasyatis thetidis*, also occurs here, especially north of Cook Strait, and can be identified by its tail being longer than the body itself.

300. Rough Skate *(Whai)*
Raja nasuta

A species easily distinguishable from other rays by its comparative thinness, long pointed snout, two dorsal fins on the tail, and absence of the long bony tail spine. It is light brown, mottled and spotted with dark brown on the top side and white beneath. The Rough Skate is common at moderate depths all round the New Zealand coast, especially in Hawke's Bay and Otago. It is usually 500-900 mm long and is an excellent food fish. Other species of skates occur in New Zealand but are mostly confined to the deeper waters on the continental slope.

301. Electric Ray *(Whai Repo)*
Torpedo fairchildi

The Electric Ray is somewhat shark-like in the tail region but the front of the body is expanded as a large flat disc. It is dark, almost black, and grows to about 1.2 m long. There is no spine on the tail, but this fish has the remarkable ability of inflicting a powerful electric shock. Beneath the skin on each side of the forward flukes of the body there are intricate cells, connected with the nervous system, which produce an electric discharge. An example caught on a line at Maraetai administered a distinct shock which was transmitted up the line to the fisherman's hands, the circuit being completed from the fact that the man's feet were immersed in the bilge water of a small boat.

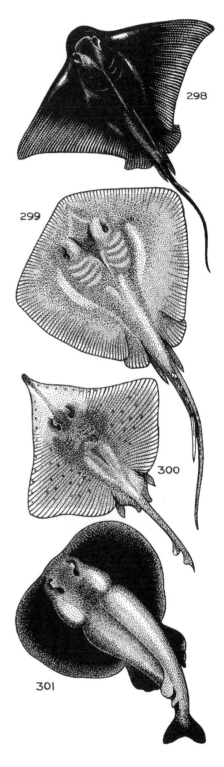

Chimaerids

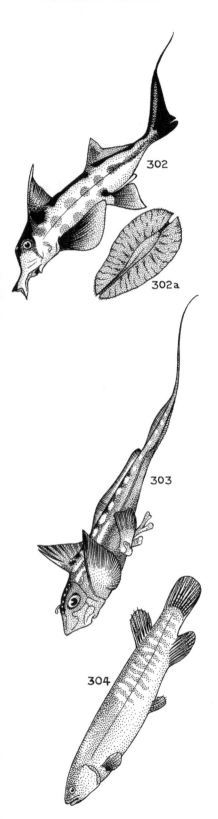

302

302a

303

304

Chimaerids (elephant fish, ghost sharks) are related to sharks and rays, and like them have a cartilagenous skeleton, not a bony one, as in the true fish. They differ, however, by having a skin-covering over the gills, with a single opening, instead of the usual five gill slits. Their skin is smooth, without rough denticles, and a single large spine precedes the first dorsal fin.

302. Elephant Fish (Reperepe)
Callorhynchus milii
The Elephant Fish are confined to the Antarctic Basin and the South Pacific Ocean. The New Zealand species grows to 0.6 m long and is common along the whole of the east coast of the South Island and occurs at times to as far north as the Bay of Plenty. An important breeding ground of this fish is off Sumner Beach, Canterbury. Here they deposit their curious eggs, which are encased in a dark-brown horny jacket up to 250 mm long (Fig. 302a), and resembling a piece of seaweed. In the centre of the egg case is a cavity in which the embryo fish develops; from one end of this cavity a passage, closed by a special valve, leads to the exterior, and it is through this passage that the young fish in due course escapes. The eggs are laid in the sand below low-water during October and November, but development is slow and hatching does not occur until about April. Large numbers of the discarded egg cases are frequently found washed ashore on Sumner Beach. The curious trunk-like proboscis of the Elephant Fish is probably an organ of touch, useful in locating buried shellfish, which form part of its food. The flesh is of good edible quality and closely resembles that of Hapuku. It requires prior soaking in fresh water to eliminate a slight ammonia taste.

303. Ghost Shark (Repe Hikuroa)
Hydrolagus novaezelandiae
A relative of the Elephant Fish but lacks the trunk-like snout and has a long tapering tail. The dark mottled fish shown here, occurs over the outer continental shelf, and is familiar to trawl fishermen. In deeper slope waters (350-1,000 m) some allied forms, the Pale Ghost Shark and the long-nosed rhinochimaeras, are found instead.

Bony Fish

The majority of fish are bony fish, at least 20,000 Recent species, with a great variety in shapes, sizes and colours. As the name indicates they all have well developed bony skeletons and a bony cover (operculum) protects their gills. Most have a protective skin-covering of scales.

304. Native Trout (Kōkopu)
Galaxias fasciatus
A secretive fish found under stones, banks and around sunken logs in bush streams throughout New Zealand. It is a dull brownish fish variously marked, when adult, with undulating pale streaks, especially towards the tail. It grows to about 250 mm long, and the body is scaleless. Together with the young of a closely related smaller and more slender fish, G. maculatus, it forms the well-known Whitebait. Before 1929 the eggs and larval history of New Zealand Whitebait were unknown. It is now known that the Kōkōpu migrates to the tidal parts of the rivers during spring tides and spawns at the highest margin amongst rushes and grasses. As the tides fall off the eggs are left high and dry and develop free from aquatic enemies. When the next spring tides reach the eggs, hatching takes place and the larvae are carried down by the ebb tide. The post larval stages of these fish are our Whitebait (or Inanga). They are an esteemed delicacy with most people. Nature's ingenious scheme for the protection of Whitebait eggs has been largely upset by the advance of agriculture, where stock and the clearing of land have destroyed their habitats.

305. Long-finned Eel (Kaiwharuwharu)
Anguilla dieffenbachii

306. Short-finned Eel (Hau)
Anguilla australis schmidtii

These are the common freshwater eels. They are much alike except for the relative length of the dorsal fin and regarding this feature the popular names are self-explanatory. The Short-finned Eel belongs mainly to the north and east and the Long-finned Eel to the south and west. New Zealand can claim to have the world's largest freshwater eels, for examples over 1.5 m long and weighing up to 20 kg are on record. These extra large eels are senile creatures that have ceased to obey the breeding urge to migrate and simply stay behind, steadily putting on weight. The remarkable migrations of the European and American eels to breeding grounds in the West Indies is now well known, but it is not generally realised that our own species indulge in a similar migration. The actual site of the oceanic breeding ground for the New Zealand eels is not accurately known, but it is thought to be in tropical or subtropical waters east of Australia. A distinctive leaf-shaped gelatinous larva hatches from eggs laid at sea. These are carried by ocean currents back to the New Zealand coast. At this time they transform into actively swimming "glass eels" which, as they migrate up streams and rivers, become pigmented. The male Short-finned Eel is called Tuna Heke and the female Papakura.

307. Conger Eel (Ngōiro)
Conger verreauxi

The common one of a number of marine eels. It grows up to 1.8 m long, with a weight of 20 kg, is restricted to salt water and is variously coloured, for it may be dark grey, pale brown, yellowish, or pale greenish. It seldom has markings, but is usually paler below. Other species of congers have elaborate patterns in red-brown, orange and grey. The remarkably slender bronzy-brown Snake-eel, *Ophisurus serpens*, attains a length of 3.6 m but its maximum diameter is no more than 55 mm.

308. Cling Fish (Papawharu)
Diplocrepis puniceus

This is found by turning over stones at low tide, for it frequently makes no attempt to escape, but clings tightly to the stone by means of a specially designed suction disc on the under side of the body. It is a small fish, only 75 mm long, with a broadly flattened body, and is bright pink marbled and spotted with red and brown.

309. Silvery Oarfish (Ika Tuna)
Regalecus glesne

This is a bizarre inhabitant of the ocean depths, which comes to the surface on rare occasions in New Zealand waters. The body is bright silver spotted with mauve, and with irregular black stripes and spots about the head. Right along the back runs a vermilion-coloured dorsal fin, and over the head there is a high crest of red rays. On the under side near the head are two long feelers with broadened tips and from these it gets its popular name of oarfish. Oarfish of several species are widely distributed, but they never occur abundantly. Their sinuous movements and great length, sometimes over 6 m, have provided more than one erroneous record of a "sea-serpent".

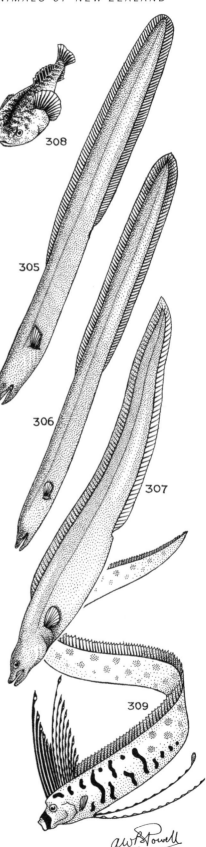

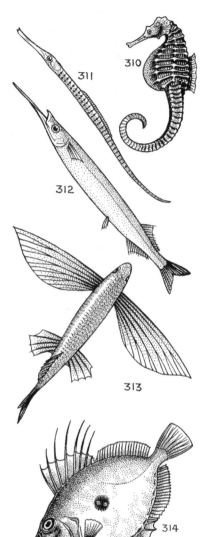

310. **Sea-horse** *(Kīore Moana)*
Hippocampus abdominalis

Not uncommon around seaweed-covered rocks in harbours throughout New Zealand. This quaint little fish grows 150-200 mm high, and is usually mottled in browns. The body is narrow and strongly cross ridged on the sides. The resemblance of the head to that of a horse is most marked, and the likeness is further strengthened by a well-formed neck and prominent chest. The tail, however, is coiled and used for attachment to seaweeds, where this little fish awaits its tiny crustacean victims, which are sucked into its tubular mouth. An alternative Māori name is Manaia.

311. **Long-snouted Pipefish** *(Ihe Ihu Roa)*
Stigmatophora macropterygia

This is slender with the tail tapered to a fine point. The mouth is long and tubular with tiny jaws at the extreme tip. The pipefish are like stretched out sea-horses, but they always remain thus and the tail is not prehensile. The figured species is usually 150-200 mm long, but they sometimes grow to 350 mm. It is greenish or brownish with two rows of dark brown dots along each side. This species is widespread throughout New Zealand and is found occasionally amongst wharf piles. A more abundant species is the smaller *Lissocampus filum* that lives among seaweeds. It is brownish with black crossbars, and has a much shorter snout.

312. **Piper** *(Takeke)*
Hyporhamphus ihi

This is common in the harbours and estuaries of both the North and South Islands. The Piper is excellent eating, and its usual mode of capture with a light rod and line and float provide sport for young and old alike. This fish grows to about 300 mm long, is narrow, and at once distinguished by its curious mouth, with the beaked lower jaw protruding much beyond the upper.

313. **Flying Fish** *(Maroro)*
Cypselurus lineatus

This grows up to 400 mm long, and is generally distributed in east coast waters from the Bay of Plenty northwards. The colour is dark steely blue on top and lighter below. The so-called wings are enlarged membranous fins, and these enable this fish to accomplish planing flights of up to 75 m at speeds of 30-45 km/hour. The reason for these flights is for eluding fast-swimming predaceous fish.

314. **John Dory** *(Kūparu)*
Zeus faber

A fish found mostly in the waters of the North Island, where it is obtained by trawling. It grows up to 500 mm long and is dirty white to dull greenish and grey with a conspicuous round black spot on each side of the body. The European Dory has these spots also, and in the early ages this feature gave rise to the tradition that this was the fish from which St. Peter obtained the tribute money, the spots being regarded as the inherited imprints of the Apostle's finger and thumb. Unfortunately for the tradition St. Peter's fish was the inhabitant of a lake. In summer the John Dory comes into shallow water and may be netted – they make curious grunting sounds on being captured. It is much esteemed as a food fish.

315. Sand Flounder (Pātiki)

Rhombosolea plebeia

One of four closely allied species of New Zealand flat-fish, two of which are commonly marketed. They are the inhabitants of shallow tidal sandy or muddy flats, but some occur in deep water also. The remarkable feature of a flat-fish is the fact that it is born with a symmetrical body, having an eye on each side of the head, but once it takes up its permanent mode of living with one side resting on the bottom the lower eye migrates and adjoins its fellow on the upper side. The common flounder with the yellow underside is the "Yellowbelly", *R. leporina* – it is commonly taken on mud-flats in harbours and in estuaries.

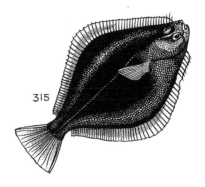

316. New Zealand Sole (Pātiki Rori)

Peltorhamphus novaezelandiae

The soles are distinguished from flounders by their oval shapes, rounded region of the head and the almost continuous fringe of fins. Most of the market supply is trawled in moderately deep water, but it is occasionally found in shallow estuarine locations. The New Zealand Sole is olive-grey, dotted with black and extra large examples have been recorded up to 600 mm long. It is esteemed as a food fish, but only because it is less common in the markets than flounder, which are superior in taste and food value. Two other species of soles may be found but they have more slender shapes and are smaller sized. In total, about sixteen species of flat-fish are known from New Zealand waters, including a large turbot, *Colistium nudipinnis*, which is comparatively rare, and the Megrim, or Witch, *Arnoglossus scapha*, which is not popular as a food fish as it is usually very thin. The latter species abounds in the Te Whanga Lagoon, Chatham Island.

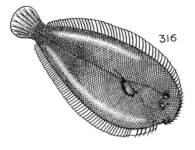

317. Yellow-eyed Mullet (Aua)

Aldrichetta forsteri

A small green-blue and silver fish often called the Sprat but it is not related to the English fish of that name. This is a common fish throughout New Zealand, and because of its schooling behaviour it can be netted on almost any beach in great quantities. The Yellow-eyed Mullet is good eating except for the annoyance occasioned by many small bones. A related species is the Grey Mullet *Mugil cephalus* which is similar in shape but does not have a bright yellow iris to the eye. In northern waters the larger Grey Mullet are a familiar sight, leaping from the water, or stirring up sediments as they feed, in harbour shallows and estuaries. They are sometimes caught commercially; muddy in flavour, but excellent when smoked.

318. Jack Mackerel (Hauture)

Trachurus novaezelandiae

One of two species in our waters with a complete lateral line covering of enlarged shield-like scales. This species prefers northern inshore waters, and is noted for its surface schooling behaviour during summer months when it can be caught commercially by purse seining methods. Younger fish are found in harbours. A favourite place for them to feed is under the wharf, attracted by the presence of Whitebait, and they can be easily caught with a line and a small hook.

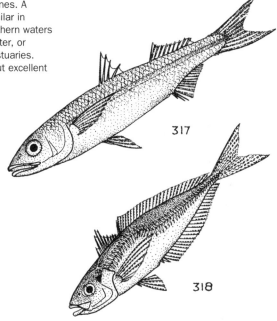

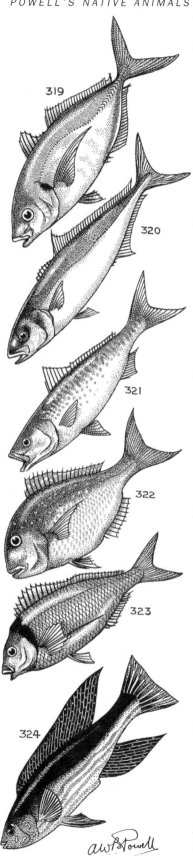

319. Trevally *(Araara)*
Pseudocaranx dentex

Once a common school fish in North Auckland waters, its population has been drastically reduced by commercial purse seining. These fish, which average about 400 mm long, move with considerable speed, but ignore all attempts at trolling. When not schooling the Trevally is easily taken by hook and line from the sea-bottom. Aged females of this species become solitary and reach a large size. One such taken at Motutapu Island, Auckland, was 880 mm long. The Trevally is recognised by its rather deep laterally compressed body, conspicuous bony spines on the lateral line towards the tail, and brilliant colouring of iridescent blue and green, paling below to iridescent silvery. The flesh is firm and very tasty, and it is surprising that its worth is not generally realised.

320. Kingfish *(Haku)*
Seriola lalandi

An excellent sporting fish which readily takes the trolling hook or spinner. It grows to about 1.5 m long, with a weight of over 55 kg, but the average examples are about 650 mm long. It is much thicker in the body than the Trevally and more rounded in cross section. In colour it is greenish-blue or purplish-blue above and silvery-white below. It feeds on small school-fish and is frequently seen pursuing them right into shallow water. Small fish often leap from the water, high and dry on the shore, in their frantic endeavours to evade the Kingfish. Fresh Kingfish is rather dry and flavourless, but it improves as a canned product.

321. Kahawai
Arripis trutta

A common school fish from Cook Strait northwards, but it is comparatively rare in the south. Although only 350-600 mm long the Kahawai is a good sporting fish, for it readily takes the spinner and fights gamely to the end. It is greenish-grey above and white below, frequently zigzag striped and spotted in brown on the upper part of the body. Half-grown Kahawai is good eating, but they tend with age to become dry and tasteless. Like the Kingfish it improves with canning, and is a fair substitute for canned salmon.

322. Snapper *(Tāmure)*
Chrysophrys auratus

The principal food fish at Auckland, but it becomes increasingly uncommon south of East Cape and Cape Egmont. The Snapper is reddish-bronze above, spotted with light blue, and silvery grey below. It has a deep body and a large head. The snapper is a great scavenger and a voracious feeder, and will eat almost anything in the way of animal food. For most of the year it is a bottom feeder, partaking of crabs, other crustacea, shellfish, heart-urchins and small fish, but from October to December those of breeding age congregate at the surface in definite areas where spawning takes place. During this period the Snapper feeds on surface organisms, especially salps, which are a floating kind of sea-squirt. The breeding ground for Auckland Snapper is between Tiri Tiri Island and Kawau Island. The average Snapper is about 350 mm long, but a huge example, 13 kg in weight and 1.04 m long, was taken years ago at Gannet Island, near Kawhia.

323. Tarakihi
Nemadactylus macropterus

This is another good food fish, common throughout New Zealand. It is about the same size as the Snapper, but has a smaller head and a long spiny ray extending from each of the pectoral or side fins. The colour is silvery grey with a black saddle behind the head.

324. Butterfish (Mararī)
Odax pullus

A kelp fish found throughout New Zealand, but most commonly in the south. It grows to about 500 mm long, is purplish grey, lighter below, and the fins are variegated with bright blue. An alternative name is "Greenbone" from the fact that the bones and the flesh in contact with them are stained bright bluish green. Young fish are yellow-brown in colour with pale blotches and in the past were thought to belong to a separate species. Butterfish graze on seaweeds, and occupy family territories within reef communities.

325. Blue Cod (Rāwaru)
Parapercis colias

An important commercial species in the South Island and excellent eating either fresh or smoked. It occurs throughout New Zealand, mainly in deep water, but the best concentrations are in Cook Strait, Stewart Island and the Chatham Islands. It grows to a length of 600 mm with a weight of 5 kg. In colour it is dark greenish to bluish-grey marbled with brown.

326. Maomao
Scorpis violaceus

This is a common fish north of East Cape. Adults are 200-350 mm long and easily recognised by their blue to violet colour, fading to bluish silvery-white below. The Maomao is usually found around sunken rocks and reefs on the open coast, and a shoal of them in clear water is a fine sight. Maomao is an excellent food fish, but as it frequents rocky ground, hook and line is the more satisfactory means of capture, hence it is seldom seen in the markets.

327. Groper (Hāpuku)
Polyprion oxygeneios

A very large deep-water species, highly esteemed throughout New Zealand as a food fish. It frequents reefs and caverns in deep water, and is remarkable for its lack of fight when hooked. Some examples attain a length of 1.5 m and a weight of over 80 kg, but the average length is about 650 mm. Most of the very large ones live at 200 m or more and are a different species, the Bass, *P. moeone*, distinguished by having a much larger head and a deeper body.

328. Yellowfin Tuna (Ahirere)
Thunnus albacares

A magnificent torpedo-shaped fish of the mackerel group, known as Tuna or Tunny. It ranges far and wide over the Pacific, for it is known from Hawaii, Japan, and northern New Zealand. A large New Zealand specimen was taken near Whangaroa in 1935 and measured 1.9 m long and weighed 84 kg. This species is dull blue above, silvery below, and the fins are bordered with bright yellow. A feature of the fish is the large sickle-shaped dorsal and anal fins.

329. Southern Bluefin Tuna (Ika Tira Iti)
Thunnus maccoyii

This is of similar size, shape and general colour to the Yellowfin Tuna, but the dorsal and anal fins are much smaller and lack the yellow border. It is one of the larger-sized tunas reaching lengths over 2.5 m and a weight greater than 400 kg. This powerful, fast-swimming, migratory tuna is widely distributed in southern oceans and is caught offshore by commercial longliners.

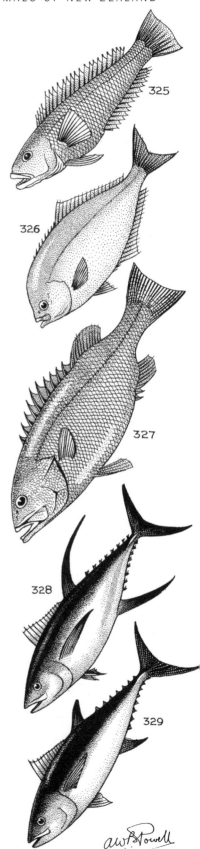

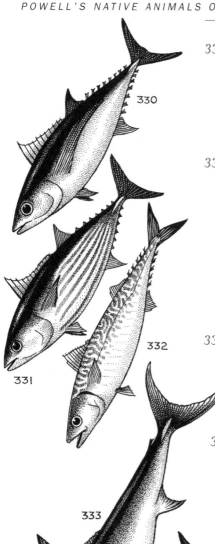

330. Albacore *(Mura Pounamu)*
Thunnus alalunga
This is at once distinguished by the very long pectoral or side fins. It grows to about 650 mm long and is a brilliant blue above and bluish silver below. This fish is not uncommon offshore around the North Auckland east coast during summer. All members of the tuna group are powerful swimmers and almost invariably they will not take the trolling hook at speeds under about 20 km/hour.

331. Skipjack Tuna *(Kawakawa)*
Katsuwonus pelamis
A widely distributed oceanic fish which comes as a summer migrant to northern New Zealand waters. It grows up to about 550 mm long and is violet blue above and pale purplish to silvery grey below with about six dark grey streaks running lengthwise. All the tuna fish achieve their speed by a sculling action of the large powerful tail. The other fins are used for manoeuvring or as stabilisers. While swimming, the dorsal fins fold back into sunken grooves, and the pectoral or side fins fit exactly into depressions in the fish's body. Because they migrate in large schools Skipjack Tuna are currently the most important commercial tuna species. Large numbers are caught by purse seining methods when schools congregate near the surface to feed on plankton.

332. Blue Mackerel *(Tawatawa)*
Scomber australasicus
Also known as English Mackerel, this species is widely distributed throughout tropical and sub-tropical Pacific waters. It is shining bluish-green on the back with spots and meandering bars of dark colour; the underside is silvery. It is a surface fish usually found in schools, and is not uncommon from Cook Strait northwards.

333. Broadbill Swordfish *(Pāea)*
Xiphias gladius
This ranges all tropical and temperate seas, but in New Zealand is a rare visitor. The Broadbill differs from the marlins in having a longer and stouter sword, which is broad and flat, a massive and permanently erect dorsal fin, and single lateral flanges on each side near the tail. It is purplish brown above and silvery white below.

334. Black Marlin *(Taketonga)*
Makaira indica
The larger of three species of marlins which have brought New Zealand into prominence as a base for excellent big-game fishing. The best grounds are off the Bay of Islands, Whangaroa, and Mayor Island. The Black Marlin is dark blue above with indistinct vertical stripes and bluish silver below. It is deeper in the body and a heavier fish than either Blue Marlin or Striped Marlin, and unlike these fish its pectoral fins cannot be folded flat against the body.

335. Striped Marlin (Takeketonga)
Tetrapturus audax

The common big-game fish of New Zealand waters, but the species ranges over most of the Pacific. It grows to about 3.5 m long with a weight of up to 180 kg, but the average is about 130 kg. It differs from the Black Marlin in having less depth to the body, more conspicuous vertical stripes and is considerably smaller. Both species visit northern New Zealand waters from December to April. Marlins differ from the Broadbill in having a retractive sail-like dorsal fin, paired flanges on each side near the tail, and curious bony extensions of the vertebrae which interlock and give both strength and flexibility to the backbone. The vertebrae in the Broadbill lack these bony interlocking structures. Marlins fight magnificently, and frequently leap clean out of the water. The flesh is good eating, having a distinctive, very palatable flavour.

336. Barracouta (Mangā)
Thyrsites atun

A long narrow fish attaining a length of almost 1.5 m and a weight of 6 kg. It is found throughout New Zealand and Australia, and may occur in surface shoals. It is predaceous on other fish and is notable for the unrelenting fury with which it attacks other fish, sometimes larger than itself. The teeth are long and pointed like needles. The upper part of the body is dark grey with bluish reflections, and the lower part silvery grey. The Barracouta is most abundant in the South Island where it is regarded as an important edible fish.

337. Frostfish (Para)
Lepidopus caudatus

This species is like a long narrow ribbon of burnished silver, 1.0-1.7 m long. They derive their name from the fact that numbers of these fish come ashore around the coast, usually on calm, clear frosty nights. No satisfactory explanation has yet been advanced for the Frostfish's apparent propensity for self-destruction. These fish are taken at times by trawlers operating in northern waters, from depths of 50-120 m, but are widely distributed in cool waters. They are more abundant west of Cape Farewell and on the Chatham Rise.

338. Ling (Hokarari)
Genypterus blacodes

This fish grows to 1.2 m long, with a weight of 20 kg, and looks just like a giant tadpole. The colour is reddish-purple, marbled and speckled in darker shades, and fading to pinkish-white below. The Ling is very abundant in deep water from Cook Strait southwards. It is a good food fish and is caught in considerable numbers by commercial long-liners.

339. Red Gurnard (Kumukumu)
Chelidonichthys kumu

Several species of gurnard occur in New Zealand but Red Gurnard is the most common. Gurnards are easily recognised by their parchment-like side fins, which resemble wings, and curious finger-like processes associated with these fins. These fingers are employed to feel the sea bottom in search of crustaceans and other animal food. Red Gurnard grows to 450 mm long, but the usual size is about 300 mm. It is largely reddish to reddish-brown, but the side fins are dark green relieved by sky-blue spots and crossed by bright red rays. It is a good food fish and occurs abundantly everywhere in New Zealand except in the extreme south.

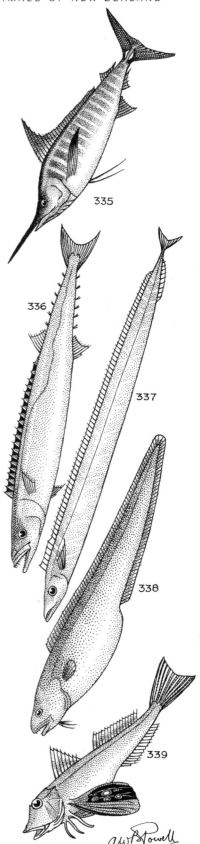

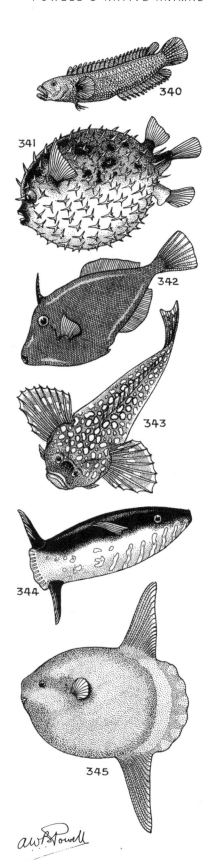

340. Rockfish *(Taumaka)*
Acanthoclinus fuscus
A small brownish-olive fish, 150-200 mm long, which is found lurking under boulders at low tide. It is an ugly fish with stout fin rays which are thickened at the ends, not tapered to a fine point as in most fish. The egg mass is a yellowish jelly-like ball, about 75 mm in diameter and usually deposited amongst sea-grass. Several other species occur here, mostly living sub-tidally to depths of about 90 m.

341. Porcupinefish *(Kōpūtōtara)*
Allomycterus jaculiferus
This belongs to a group of poisonous tropical fish, most of which have the power of greatly inflating the body as a means of defence. When the body is thus inflated long spines embedded in the skin become rigid and erect. This fish, which is often well over 300 mm long, is frequently trawled in North Island waters. It is white variously blotched and spotted with brown and yellow.

342. Leather-jacket *(Kōkiri)*
Parika scaber
A curious rough-skinned fish with a small mouth and a trigger-like spine on the back which can be locked into a vertical position at will. This fish resembles brown suede leather except for the fins, which are bright yellow. It is a good food fish and is sold in the Auckland markets in the form of skinned fillets under the name of "Cream-fish". The Leather-jacket is under 300 mm long and is common in the outer Hauraki Gulf, where they are often seen feeding amongst seaweed-covered rocks.

343. Spotted Stargazer *(Kūtoro)*
Geniagnus monopterygius
An ugly fish with a broad depressed body and the mouth inclined upwards. It grows up to 300 mm long and is dark brown or grey, mottled with oval to crescentic light spots. This fish is sluggish, for it lurks amongst rocks or shingle on the sea-bottom, ready to seize and devour any crustacean or small fish that comes within reach of the cavernous mouth. It is found in low-tidal rock pools, shallow harbours, and in deeper water. Normally it lives buried in sand or mud, with just the eyes, mouth, and top of the head showing.

344. Oblong Sunfish *(Mātua)*
Ranzania laevis
This sunfish is little more than 300 mm long and is specially designed for deep vertical diving. The dorsal and ventral fins as well as the short fringed tail are all bunched at the end of the body. This is a great rarity, known from New Zealand by only a few specimens. Its distribution is thought to be worldwide but nowhere is it common. On the rare occasions when it makes its appearance at Honolulu the native people regard it as the fish god ancestor of the mackerels and bonitos and on no account must it be molested.

345. Ocean Sunfish *(Rātāhuihui)*
Mola mola
A giant compared with the last species, for it grows up to 4 m high with a length of 2.9 m and a weight of over 2,000 kg. These giant fish are not uncommon in New Zealand waters, and from time to time odd ones become stranded in shallow water. They have a small mouth and are harmless, for they feed on squids and other small marine creatures.

Amphibians

Amphibians are the oldest and least advanced group of land vertebrates. Their ancestors, many millions of years ago, emerged from swamps and ponds to exploit the possibilities of life on dry land. This transition is still apparent in the development of the frog, which recapitulates past history by undergoing a metamorphosis from a tailed swimming tadpole to an adult tail-less frog, which can live both on land and in the water. The word "amphibia" is from two Greek words meaning "both" and "life" and refers to this dual existence. The only native New Zealand amphibia are three uncommon species of small frogs.

346. Hochstetter's Frog (Pēpeke)
Leiopelma hochstetteri.

A hundred years ago New Zealanders were unaccustomed to the croaking of frogs. The frogs now abundant in swamps and ponds throughout the country are not native but are introduced Australian species. Our native frogs are known from a few localities only and they are far from common. There are three species of native frogs: *L. hochstetteri* from several northern North Island mountain ranges; Archey's Frog *L. archeyi* from the Coromandel Range; and Hamilton's Frog *L. hamiltoni* from Stephens and Maud Islands (Cook Strait area). They are small, seldom exceeding 40 mm long, and are mottled dark and light brown. These frogs frequent the vicinity of mountain streams or under stones and logs on the higher ridges. Native frogs have a modified life history in which there is no free-swimming tadpole stage, but a minute tailed frog emerges straight from the egg. Eggs are laid in damp muddy sites, not in standing water.

Reptiles

Reptiles are represented in New Zealand by some 45 species of small lizards, two sea-snakes and five turtles, which stray occasionally to our shores, and the remarkable Tuatara, a unique surviving member of an archaic group which became extinct elsewhere many millions of years ago.

Reptiles are cold-blooded vertebrates with a scaly skin, and they breathe by lungs, but of less complex form than those of birds and mammals. They are more advanced than the amphibia, since the land members do not require to spend their early existence in water.

Reptiles were once the dominant land animals, and many of them achieved a great size. It is interesting to note that the marine turtles come to land to lay their eggs, thus reversing the procedure of the amphibia.

Reptiles develop from hard-shelled eggs, or they may be born alive. Birds and mammals arose from reptilian stock, and so we find that the birds continue the egg-laying habit and the mammals, except for the most primitive, give birth to active young.

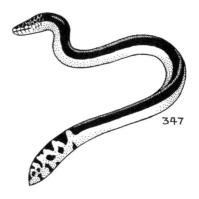

347. Yellow-bellied Sea-snake (Moko Ngata Moana)
Pelamis platurus

A visitor to our shores from the tropical Pacific. It grows up to 1 m long and is easily distinguished from the conger-eels by the flattened end of its tail and the conspicuous colour pattern. The upper half of the body is black and the lower portion yellow with large black spots near the end of the tail. This species is highly venomous, but the fangs are small. There are numerous records of this snake from North Auckland waters, but they are usually found either washed ashore or in a spent condition.

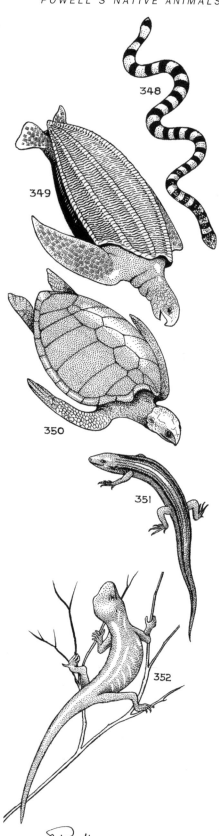

348. **Banded Sea-snake** (*Moko Ngata Moana Mōwhiti*)
Laticauda colubrina

A rare visitor to North Auckland waters. It grows to 1.4 m long, but is slender and circular in section, the end of the tail alone being flattened. The general colour is bluish-grey conspicuously marked with numerous broad rings of dark brown. It is venomous, but has very small jaws. The species is widely distributed, for it occurs from the Bay of Bengal to Japan, Australia and throughout the tropical Pacific.

349. **Leathery Turtle** (*Honu Hiwihiwi*)
Dermochelys coriacea

This turtle is the sole survivor of a group of fossil species differing from all other living species in the form of the carapace or "shell" which is a mosaic-like structure of a large number of closely-joined, irregular, bony discs, covered by a leathery exterior, having several prominent longitudinal keels. When partly submerged it looks just like an upturned dinghy. This species is widely distributed throughout the tropical Atlantic, Indian and Pacific Oceans, from which it wanders to the cooler regions. Yearly becoming scarcer around the world, Leathery Turtles are actually quite often seen in New Zealand waters, mainly in the north, but as far south as Foveaux Strait. They can reach 2.8 m total length with a weight of 680 kg.

350. **Loggerhead Turtle** (*Honu*)
Caretta caretta

Related to the Green Turtle *Chelonia mydas* and Hawksbill Turtle *Eretmochelys imbricata,* all of which are occasional visitors to New Zealand waters. They have a thick, bony shell covered with large, closely-fitting smooth plates of "tortoise"-shell. The shell may grow to 1.5 m long.

351. **Common Skink** (*Mokopapa*)
Oligosoma nigriplantare

This is the sleek brownish mottled lizard common under stones and logs, in most areas south of Lake Taupo. In the Auckland district the commonest species is the Copper Skink *Cyclodina aenea*. These are the little lizards of our gardens which dart away at great speed when disturbed. Our lizards are either skinks or geckos. The former have small heads, are smooth and scaly all over and live on the ground, while the latter have broad heads, a soft granular skin and are found among the foliage of trees and shrubs, or on the ground. One of the best known peculiarities of the lizards is their ability to cast off a large portion of the tail when disturbed, apparently without ill effect. A new tail eventually grows and is usually slightly different in colour pattern. The breaking off of the tail without severe injury to the lizard is due to the presence of cartilaginous bands between certain of the tail vertebrae, making intentional points of weakness.

352. **Common Green Gecko** (*Kākāriki*)
Naultinus elegans

A most handsome lizard, about 150 mm long, and normally a velvety bright grass green. Occasionally sulphur yellow ones are seen, and examples with varied patterns of both colours are not uncommon. This lizard is not often seen, for in its natural haunts the protective colouring renders it most inconspicuous amongst the foliage of shrubs and small bushes. The species is widely distributed in New Zealand, and they are often found on manuka scrub.

353. *Tuatara*
Sphenodon punctatus

A reptile up to 600 mm long which still exists on some 30 islands off the North Auckland east coast, Bay of Plenty and Cook Strait. Tuataras once occurred on the mainland, but have long disappeared. The Tuatara is not a lizard, but the sole survivor of a group of ancient reptiles. It is a "living fossil", one of the most remarkable instances of the survival of a group which elsewhere became extinct many millions of years ago. The Tuatara has a strange habit of sharing the occupation of petrel burrows. The bird forms the burrow and in summer petrel and Tuatara occupy it jointly, but in winter when the petrel goes to sea the Tuatara is left in undisputed possession. The nesting petrel does not seem to object to the presence of the Tuatara in its burrow – during the day they both sleep, and at night when the petrel wakes, the Tuatara sets out on its nocturnal hunt for insects. The Tuatara has many primitive features; beneath the skin on the head is the pineal gland which is considered to be the remnant of a "third eye", and the jaw does not possess socketed teeth, but merely serrations of the jawbone. There are records of Tuataras kept in captivity for over 50 years, and in the wild some may live for over 100 years. The Tuatara is absolutely protected.

353

Birds

A thousand years of Polynesian occupation and 150 years of European influence have wrought great changes in the New Zealand bird fauna. Many species that once occurred in countless thousands have dwindled greatly with the depletion of the indigenous forests. A few have adapted both to cultivated surroundings and to the keen competition from some 30 species introduced from Australia and the northern hemisphere. In districts under cultivation it is the introduced species that are almost invariably in evidence – the native species must be sought in their natural surroundings of bush, swamp and shore. Our native bird fauna consists of about 300 species and includes some unique flightless species and remarkable migrants. Our bird fauna has descended partly from ancient stock derived before the isolation of the New Zealand land mass, partly from widely distributed southern sea birds, and partly from species that have successfully colonised from Australia (and continue to do so).

354. *Brown Kiwi* (Kiwi)
Apteryx australis

The kiwi has become so widely known as a symbol of New Zealand that description is scarcely necessary. It is a rather small, sturdily built, flightless bird, noted for its long beak, with the nostrils at the tip, a position unique among living birds. The wings are rudimentary, the tail absent, the feathers barbless like hairs, and it lays one or two enormous eggs out of all proportion to the size of the bird. The Brown Kiwi stands about 300 mm high and its plumage is largely dark reddish-brown streaked with black. Formerly it was widespread, but it is now comparatively rare and confined to the more extensive forest areas of Northland, the central North Island, Fiordland and Stewart Island. It is a nocturnal bird frequenting the dense damp recesses of the forest where the soft ground and rotting leaves enable it to probe its long beak in search of worms, large grubs and larvae. The kiwi nests in holes beneath the roots of trees or in steep banks in the forest. One egg is usual, but frequently two are laid. The egg is approximately 125 mm by 80 mm, truly remarkable for a bird no larger than a domestic fowl. There are two other species of kiwi. The Great Spotted Kiwi (*Apteryx haastii*) is now confined to the north-west of the South Island, and the Little Spotted Kiwi (*A. owenii*) is reduced to an introduced population on Kapiti Island. (Not figured.)

354

Penguins are a fascinating group of birds of southern ocean origin, remarkable for their adaptation of the wings into flippers, designed for swimming. The feathers are reduced to small scale-like structures.

355. King Penguin (Pokotiwha)
Aptenodytes patagonicus

The most handsome of the penguins inhabiting the New Zealand area. It is a fine erect bird about 600 mm high, strikingly coloured with greenish-black head, silky white breast, pale blue and speckled black back and a deep golden yellow belt across the throat and neck. The species is widely distributed in the subantarctic waters of Tierra del Fuego, Falkland Islands and South Georgia, but in the New Zealand region the one breeding colony is on Macquarie Island. Stragglers are sometimes seen on the other islands of the New Zealand subantarctic, Stewart Island and the coasts of Otago.

356. Blue Penguin (Kororā)
Eudyptula minor

Common all around the coasts of the North and South Islands, Stewart Island and the Chathams. It is never seen far from land, and during August and September comes ashore on isolated parts of the coast to nest in rocky caverns and burrows. The food of this penguin consists of small fish and various marine organisms which it pursues under water with the speed and agility of a voracious fish.

357. Wandering Albatross (Toroa)
Diomedea exulans

This is one of nine magnificent albatrosses found in New Zealand waters. These birds range the vast turbulent southern ocean, but at least seven of them nest regularly on selected breeding grounds either among the southern islands of New Zealand or at the Chatham Islands. *Diomedea epomophora*, the Royal Albatross, nests in small numbers at Taiaroa Head, near Dunedin. There is no other instance of a breeding colony of albatrosses adjacent to a large city. The Wandering Albatross has a wing spread of about 3 m, and is common offshore throughout New Zealand, especially to the south of the main islands. It has a white head with an irregular brown patch on the crown, the back is white marked with transverse zigzag bars of grey or brown, the wings are slaty-black above, mottled with white along the edges and are mostly white underneath. The tail is black or white tipped with black. The Royal Albatross is almost entirely silvery white except for black wing tips. The beak of the albatross is very stout and strong, and is conspicuously hooked at the tip. Their apparently effortless soaring and gliding flight is a wonderful aerial achievement.

358. Giant Petrel (Pāngurunguru)
Macronectes giganteus

The largest of the petrels, having a wing spread of about 2 m. Petrels are allied to the albatrosses, and are distinguished mainly by differences in the structure of the beak. The Giant Petrel is dark slaty-brown. To sailors it is known as the Nelly or Stinkpot. The species ranges the whole of the southern ocean and it breeds on most of the subantarctic islands, including those of the New Zealand area. It is frequently seen following the inter-island ferries in Cook Strait. In stormy weather this bird is often seen in the Hauraki Gulf and occasionally in Auckland Harbour.

359. Sooty Shearwater (Tītī)
Puffinus griseus

This species was, and still is in the south, an important item in the diet of the Māori people. Thousands of young birds are taken annually from breeding grounds off the coast of Stewart Island. The birds are split, salted and preserved in their own fat in bags made from sections of the Giant Kelp. The Sooty Shearwater or Mutton Bird has an immense range over the whole of the southern ocean and at times extends to as far north as Alaska. In New Zealand this bird is commonly seen in great flocks in coastal waters. It is blackish brown with bluish-grey feet and is slightly larger than a domestic pigeon.

360. Fairy Prion (Tītī Wainui)
Pachyptila turtur

This is the small dove-grey petrel which skims the surface of the sea in its energetic quest for food. Until the white under-surface shows, when they wheel in flight, these birds are scarcely visible against the sea. This petrel, along with many others found in our seas, nests in deep burrows formed in the soft humus on offshore islands.

361. Pied Shag (Kāruhiruhi)
Phalacrocorax varius

This is a common coastal species from North Cape to Stewart Island, and is distinguished from the other species of New Zealand shags by its greenish-black back and white breast which continues to above the eyes. The Pied Shag builds large, untidy nests in trees overhanging cliff faces. Its food consists principally of fish taken along the sea coast, and it seldom goes inland.

362. Australasian Bittern (Matuku)
Botaurus poiciloptilus

This is a bird of the swamps and lagoons throughout the country, but now less common than formerly owing to the advance of settlement. It closely resembles the herons in shape, but the plumage is buff to brownish, speckled and barred with dark-brown. A conspicuous feature is the ruff of feathers around the neck. It feeds on insects, eels, rats and mice.

363. Australasian Gannet (Tākapu)
Morus serrator

This is common around the coasts of the North Island. Its high vertical dives into the sea are a frequent sight and almost invariably some small fish becomes a victim. Gannets nest on outlying islands in large colonies of most regular arrangement. This is achieved by each bird nesting as close as possible to a neighbouring nest, yet just out of range of the powerful beaks of its companions. The best known gannet colony is at Cape Kidnappers, Hawke's Bay. The young gannet is hatched naked and black, but soon becomes a ball of pure white down. Immature birds are speckled with dark grey and white, but the adult is white except for black wing and tail feathers and a golden brown patch on the head and back of the neck.

364. Grey Duck (Pārera)
Anas superciliosa

This is the common brownish native duck found throughout New Zealand. It frequents fresh waters everywhere and feeds largely on insects, crustaceans, shellfish and even aquatic plants and their seeds. It is an excellent table bird and is shot under licence seasonally.

365. Paradise Shelduck (Pūtangitangi)
Tadorna variegata

This is a handsome bird variously mottled, freckled and lined with brown and white on a brownish to black ground. The head and neck are black, shot with bluish-green in the male (illustrated), and are pure white in the female. This species is generally distributed in the South Island and over the lower half of the North Island. Its food consists of soft grasses, herbs and insects.

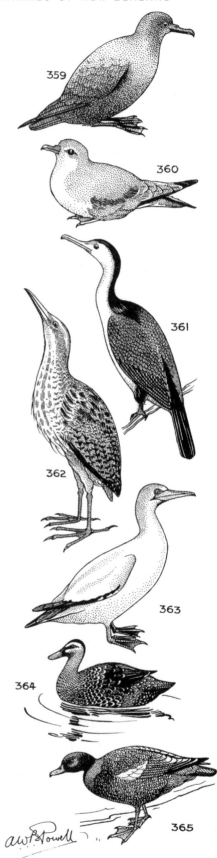

77

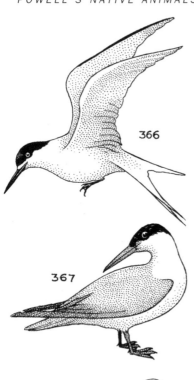

366. *White-fronted Tern (Tara)*
Sterna striata

This is abundant all around the New Zealand coasts and occurs in Tasmania and eastern Australia as well. This is the graceful little "Kahawai-bird" or "Sea-swallow", which pursues schools of small surface fish, wheeling, darting and dipping to the water, in its energetic quest for food. Since the Kahawai fish is predacious on the small school fish also, the tern is an excellent indicator of the presence of Kahawai. The cry of the tern is a single sharp note frequently sounded. In colour these birds are pale grey above and white below, with a conspicuous black cap on the head. It has a rather long white forked tail, but the body of the bird is smaller than that of the Red-billed Gull. Nesting colonies of these terns are found in early summer on sandy flats and rocks off the sea coast, often only a few metres above high-water mark.

367. *Caspian Tern (Taranui)*
Sterna caspia

This is a larger and more solidly built bird than the White-fronted Tern. It is distinguished also by its strong red bill, but has a similar black patch on the head and is also pale grey above and white below. This bird may be seen in small numbers around our coasts and sometimes inland. The Caspian Tern has an immense range extending over Europe, Asia, North America, Africa, Malaya and Australia. In New Zealand it nests about November on remote shingle beds and sandy beaches.

368. *Red-billed Gull (Tarapunga)*
Larus novaehollandiae

This is abundant throughout New Zealand, Australia and New Caledonia. This is the small grey and white gull with black and white wing tips and red bill and feet. This gull is a scavenger in harbours and at times goes inland to devour insects in the wake of the plough. It nests during early summer on rocky islands off the coast. A related species, the Black-billed Gull (*Larus bulleri*), is very similar except for the black bill and dark feet, but it frequents the inland fresh waters. It is common at Lake Rotorua and especially in Canterbury.

369. *Black-backed Gull (Karoro)*
Larus dominicanus

This is easily distinguished from either the Red-or the Black-billed Gulls by its much larger size, approximately that of a duck, and conspicuous black and white plumage in the adult. The young birds are mottled and streaked with buff and brown, and it takes $3^1/_2$ years before the adult plumage is completely assumed, then the back and top of the wings are black except for white bars at the tips of the primary feathers. The bill is yellow and the feet greenish yellow. The Black-backed Gull is widely distributed in the southern hemisphere. In New Zealand it congregates in harbours, especially near freezing works, where it gorges itself on offal. Extensive breeding colonies form up in November.

370. *Pied Stilt (Waewae Tōrea)*
Himantopus himantopus

This is widely distributed in both the North and South Islands of New Zealand. Its favourite haunts are tidal mudflats and inland swamps and lagoons. It stands about 350 mm high, but is a small-bodied bird and the legs are very long and slender. The back and back of the head are black, the tail feathers smoky grey and the rest white. The beak is very long and thin and the head distinctly rounded. The long legs of this bird are admirably suited to its wading habits. On mudflats Pied Stilts occur in large numbers, especially towards low water, stalking up and down at the water's edge in search of food. Owing to a tidal difference in Auckland of almost three hours between the Waitemata and Manukau Harbours these birds frequently fly backwards and forwards to gain a lengthened period of low tidal feedings. Their cry is like the shrill yelp of a small pup and while on the wing their long legs trail behind. They nest in September and October, usually inland on river flats or near lagoons and swamps.

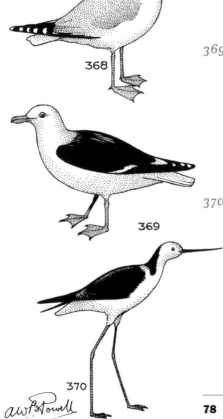

371. Banded Dotterel *(Pohowera)*
Charadrius bicinctus

This is a characteristic little bird of the sand dunes, river beds and tussock-clad plains. As one approaches, it more often runs ahead in a zigzag manner, than flies. It is about the size of a starling and in coloration is largely greyish-brown on the back and white below, with a band of black across the breast and one of chestnut lower down. It is widespread in New Zealand and occurs also in Tasmania and Australia, but the only known breeding places are in New Zealand. The eggs are dark greenish-yellow, heavily spotted and blotched with dark brown. Little effort is made to conceal the nest, which is often just a hollow in the sand, either in the open or near a clump of tussock, but nevertheless the nests are not easily located for the eggs seem to merge perfectly with the surroundings.

372. Godwit *(Kūaka)*
Limosa lapponica

This is our best known migrant. The route is from Alaska and Siberia via Japan, China and the Philippines to New Zealand where they arrive in October and November. They depart on the northward migration during March and April. It seems probable that these birds make non-stop flights between northern Australia and New Zealand. Much publicity has been given to the alleged spectacular departure of the Godwits from the extreme north of New Zealand, but in fact large flocks of Godwits are on the move most of the time, ranging from one local feeding ground to another, and a mass departure from our shores has not as yet been witnessed. Although the Godwit is essentially a summer migrant to our shores many remain throughout the year. The Godwit nests in Alaska, Siberia and eastern Asia during the latter part of May, the young birds are flying by the middle of July and the migration commences in August. This bird is easily recognised by its speckled brown plumage and long slender black beak which is slightly tilted upwards. Godwits are plentiful throughout New Zealand but especially in our northern harbours, where there are extensive tidal flats. These birds were an important article of food for the Māori and were keenly sought by sportsmen also, but they are now absolutely protected.

373. Weka
Gallirallus australis

This is slightly smaller than the Domestic Hen, a tawny brownish and blackish streaked bird with degenerate wings making it incapable of flight. It can run with great speed, but is most inquisitive and will venture very close to habitations with a stealthy gait and an enquiring demeanour. It has a habit of carrying away small shining objects such as spoons, and bushmen complain that even watches have been purloined. The figured bird is the North Island Weka, but there are three other races in the South and Stewart Islands. The North Island Weka, once abundant everywhere, has now disappeared from most districts, largely due to the depredations of Dogs, Cats, Stoats and Weasels. The Weka conceals its nest in thick scrub and lays four large eggs, creamy white with scattered reddish-brown and purplish blotches.

374. Pūkeko
Porphyrio porphyrio

This is a truly handsome bird over 0.5 m tall; indigo blue and black with white tail and red beak and legs. It is common in the swamps of both the North and South Islands and is conspicuous against the bright green background of the Raupo. It usually struts about, but can run rapidly and fly short distances. It feeds largely upon the soft shoots and roots of water plants. The nest is a large untidy construction about 300 mm high, and is located amongst Raupo or rushes in a swamp. The Takahe *(Porphyrio mantelli)*, long believed extinct but rediscovered in Fiordland in 1948, is a giant relative of the Pūkeko, which it closely resembles. (Not figured.)

375. *Australasian Harrier* (Kāhu)
Circus approximans

This is the common bird-of-prey of the countryside. It soars in wide circles with a slow steady flight, often remaining on the wing for hours, but ever watchful for food. All kinds of animal food, either dead or alive, are taken by the Harrier. The plumage is mostly brownish, streaked and barred with dark-brown and reddish-brown. It is commonly referred to as the Hawk. A rarer species, the New Zealand Falcon *Falco novaeseelandiae*, frequents the forested high country and some of the offshore islands. The Harrier breeds in swampy areas and the nest is often found in a large clump of Toetoe. These birds are ferocious from birth, for the more advanced young often devour their weaker brethren.

376. *Morepork* (Ruru)
Ninox novaeseelandiae

This is a New Zealand native owl. It feeds largely on insects and will also kill and devour rats and mice, and the occasional small bird. The nocturnal eerie "morepork" cry so often heard, even in suburban gardens, is by no means unpleasant. By day the Morepork seeks the dark masses of foliage and if disturbed glides to another spot with noiseless flight. It is nearly 300 mm tall and is mainly dark chocolate-brown streaked and spotted with light brown. The breast is light brown barred with dark brown. The nest is usually in a hollow tree.

377. *Reef Heron* (Matuku Moana)
Egretta sacra

This is a graceful dark slaty-grey bird with long beak and legs of bright yellow. It stands about 600 mm tall and is to be seen actively searching for food on the rocky foreshore of estuaries and sheltered bays. It has a leisurely droopy-winged flight. This species occurs throughout New Zealand and ranges as far away as Burma, Japan and the eastern Pacific. It nests in small caves on the seashore and lays a clutch of two or three greenish-blue eggs.

378. *White Heron* (Kōtuku)
Egretta alba

This is a stately white bird larger than the Reef Heron. The beak is bright yellow and the feet black. Adult White Herons have beautiful long white plumes down the back – these are the "ospreys" which once commanded high prices when feminine fashion placed them in demand. This heron frequents lakes, margins of rivers, swamps and sometimes the sea beach, where it feeds on small fish and eels, but it is not common in New Zealand. Its range includes Australia, Asia, Africa and Europe. The only known breeding place for this bird in New Zealand is at Okarito in South Westland. Solitary examples have a habit of wintering in widely separate localities.

379. *Long-tailed Cuckoo* (Koekoeā)
Eudynamys taitensis

A spring migrant which arrives in this country in October and leaves again in February and March, overwintering mainly from Fiji to the Society Islands. The Long-tailed Cuckoo reaches most parts of New Zealand, but is never so abundant as the Shining Cuckoo. It is a larger bird than the Shining Cuckoo, has a long tail, and the plumage is conspicuously spotted and barred in dark-brown and reddish-brown. The Long-tailed Cuckoo parasitises three of our smaller native birds (the Whitehead, Yellowhead and Brown Creeper) by introducing its egg into their nest. Once the egg hatches the young cuckoo soon acquires sufficient strength to tip the host's own eggs or young out of the nest, and it is reared alone by the foster-parents. The Long-tailed Cuckoo has a diet of insects and lizards.

380. Shining Cuckoo (Pīpīwharauroa)
Chrysococcyx lucidus

Another spring migrant, which arrives in September or October and departs in January and February, overwintering on New Britain and the Solomon Islands. It is about the size of a House Sparrow and differs noticeably from the Long-tailed Cuckoo in having a comparatively short tail. The plumage is most attractive, green, shot with purple and copper on the back and with golden-green broad bands across the white underparts of the body. Its food consists almost entirely of insects. It has the same parasitic habits as the Long-tailed Cuckoo, the Grey Warbler being the host (except on the Chathams where the Chatham Island Warbler is parasitised).

381. New Zealand Pigeon (Kererū)
Hemiphaga novaeseelandiae

This is the most handsome and characteristic bird of the forest. Its fearlessness and rustling flight soon betray its presence. It is a large plump bird about 500 mm tall, with a white breast, green head, coppery green to greyish green back and a brown tail with a greenish lustre. It feeds largely upon the berries of forest trees, particularly those of the Tawa, Miro, Kahikatea, Konini and Pūriri. The Māori were very fond of eating the Kererū and snared great numbers of them by setting up wooden drinking troughs in the forest. The birds became very thirsty when feeding and soon found the troughs. They were caught by the neck in nooses which the Māori set over the troughs. Both Māori and the early European settlers took a heavy toll of the Pigeons, but since they are now rigidly protected by law there are still ample survivors throughout the country.

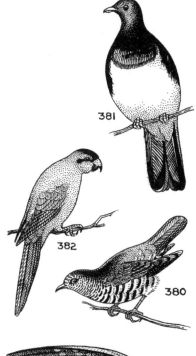

381

382. Red-crowned Parakeet (Kākāriki)
Cyanoramphus novaezelandiae

This is a handsome long-tailed bird about 280 mm long. It is mostly grass-green except for crimson patches on the head and rump and a blue and black tail. This bird was once very abundant throughout New Zealand, but is now restricted to the dense forests and offshore islands. Another parrot, the introduced Australian Eastern Rosella, is now common in several areas, particularly throughout Northland and in the Auckland area. It may damage fruit and grain whereas the native species feeds on forest berries and seeds. Other parakeets native to New Zealand are the Yellow-crowned and Antipodes Island Parakeets.

382

380

383. Kākā
Nestor meridionalis

A large, plump-bodied parrot about 450 mm long. It occurs in forested areas of the three main islands. The plumage is mostly olive brown and grey, speckled and barred with dark-brown and with crimson patches under the wings and on the rump. The food of the Kākā consists of grubs and the larvae of moths and beetles. They are noisy birds, the harsh cry resembling the Māori name Kākā, which is a phonetic rendering of the sound. The Kākā is a sprightly bird; it climbs rapidly, hops on the ground and often performs acrobatics on the wing.

383

Kea Nestor notabilis

This is slightly larger than the Kākā, but similar in most respects except for a longer beak. The prevailing colour is dull green with the under sides of the wings scarlet. The Kea belongs to the mountainous country of the South Island. It is an inquisitive and entertaining bird and on rare occasions it forsakes its normal diet of insects, grubs, worms and vegetable substance in favour of the fat and flesh of both dead and living sheep. It is the only instance of a parrot with carnivorous tendencies. (Not figured.)

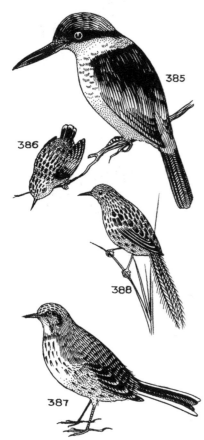

384. Kākāpo
Strigops habroptilus

A heavy-bodied parrot which is much larger than either the Kākā or the Kea. This apparently clumsy bird is incapable of flight, but can climb with agility. Once widespread, it became restricted to Fiordland and Stewart Island, but the last birds were moved to predator-free offshore islands by the Department of Conservation. The plumage is yellowish-green and brownish-buff, mottled and barred with black. The Kākāpo feeds largely on vegetation and it nests either in rock crevices or in holes under the roots of forest trees.

385. Kingfisher (Kōtare)
Halcyon sancta

This is abundant near the sea, where it feeds largely on crabs and other inhabitants of the mud flats. Inland, the Kingfisher prefers the open country and vicinity of freshwater streams to the depths of the forest. Its food in inland localities consists largely of insects and lizards. Our kingfisher is a handsome bird with deep green or blue head, back, wings and tail, contrasting with the light buff of the neck, throat and breast. The nest is sometimes in a natural hole in a tree, but more often the bird excavates a tunnel with its bill in a steep clay bank. The tunnel is 300 mm or more deep, terminating in a spacious chamber, where the clutch of 5-7 white eggs is laid, usually from November to early January. Woe betide the unwary person who places his hand in the burrow, for the Kingfisher has a powerful bill. On the whole Kingfishers are most useful birds to the agriculturalist, for they consume large quantities of grubs and insects.

386. Rifleman (Tītitipounamu)
Acanthisitta chloris

This is our smallest bird, being only 80 mm long. The Rifleman is essentially a bird of the deep forests and higher altitudes, and is especially characteristic of beech forests. The food of the Rifleman consists of small insects which it diligently searches for on the trunks and branches of trees.

387. New Zealand Pipit (Pīhoihoi)
Anthus novaeseelandiae

This is a common bird throughout the country. It is readily recognised by its habit of continuing to fly short distances ahead as one approaches, and by giving a flick of the tail every now and then as it watches the advance of an intruder. The two outer feathers on either side of the tail are white, otherwise the bird is light brownish and speckled like a Skylark. The Pipit is essentially a bird of the open country, and with the clearing of large tracts of forest it is now much more abundant than formerly. It is one of the few instances of a native species that has gained through the advance of civilisation. The nest is made on the ground, generally in a clump of tussock or similar growth.

388. Fernbird (Mātātā)
Bowdleria punctata

A small brownish striped and speckled bird with curious tail feathers, having disconnected barbs, so that each looks like a delicate fern frond. The Fernbird lives in the Raupo swamps, and is now quite scarce since large areas of swamp have been drained and brought under cultivation. This bird has a curious double-note cry which sounds like "U-tick".

389. Grey Warbler *(Riroriro)*

Gerygone igata

This is a small grey bird abundant in all parts of New Zealand. The Grey Warbler is more readily noticed by its pleasant song than by its rather drab appearance. The song is a pleasant trill, sometimes in descending at other times alternating bars. The nest is large for so small a bird, a neatly made pear-shaped structure with a circular opening in the side, the whole suspended from an outer branch of a small tree. The nest is often parasitised by the Shining Cuckoo which removes an egg and lays one of its own. The young cuckoo pushes out the warbler eggs, or young, which in any case have little chance of getting food while the cuckoo is in the nest.

390. Fantail *(Pīwakawaka)*

Rhipidura fuliginosa

This pleasant little bird requires no description. It is common throughout the country, and its numbers have in no way suffered through the advance of civilisation. It sometimes enters houses and performs its acrobatics in pursuit of flies. The nest is a beautifully woven structure of fine grass, moss, rootlets, and cobwebs, lined with hair.

391. Tui

Prosthemadera novaeseelandiae

The most characteristic bird of the forest treetops. Its vigorous melodious notes are well known to all. The song varies in different districts and is remarkable for the great variety of musical notes interspersed with curious sounds like coughs, gurglings and sneezes. The rich metallic dark green and blue plumage, relieved by the pair of white tufts on the throat, make the Tui one of our most handsome birds. Its food consists of insects, nectar and berries. During recent years the Tui has been induced to visit suburban gardens through the planting of Australian flowering gums, which provide nectar.

392. Silvereye *(Pihipihi)*

Zosterops lateralis

A pleasant sleek little yellowish-olive bird with a greyish-white breast and silver ring round the eyes now abundant throughout New Zealand, but before about 1856 it was unknown in this country. This bird is widely distributed in Australia, but what factor caused the forerunners of the New Zealand population to brave the Tasman is still a mystery. The food of the Silvereye consists of insects, nectar and soft fruits.

393. Bellbird *(Korimako)*

Anthornis melanura

This is largely yellowish-olive to olive green, smaller than the Tui, and remarkable for its glorious song which, when sung in unison, by dozens of birds together, is an experience one treasures for a lifetime. The song is a chime of four flute-like notes which is admirably adapted to a continuous rhythm. Like the Tui, the Bellbird is in the honeyeater family of birds which have brush-tipped tongues for lapping nectar. However it also eats insects and berries.

394. *Huia*
Heteralocha acutirostris

This is now extinct, but it belonged to the dense forested ranges of the North Island from the Kaimanawas to the Tararuas. This bird was larger than a Tui, uniformly black with a greenish gloss, except for a broad white band at the tip of the tail. These tail feathers were highly prized by Māori chiefs, who wore them in the hair as a symbol of their rank. A remarkable feature of these birds is the differently shaped beaks for each sex. The male had a rather straight stout beak used for chiselling away bark and rotten wood in search of grubs, while the female had a long slender curved beak with which she probed more delicately into the cavities excavated by her mate. The last authentic record of living Huias was in the Tararua Range on 28 December 1907.

395. *Kōkako*
Callaeas cinerea

A moderately large dark bluish-grey bird with a stout black bill, long black legs and conspicuous wattles of bright blue (North Island race) or orange (South Island race). It is still found in a few localities in the middle and northern portions of the North Island, but the South Island population is probably extinct.

Mammals

Mammals are highly developed, warm-blooded, backboned animals. They range in size from tiny mice and shrews to the whales, largest of all living creatures. To many people the term animal is applied in a restricted sense solely to the mammals, but actually the name animal should refer broadly to every organism not a plant or microbe.

Long isolation from other lands in the geological past has left New Zealand almost devoid of native land mammals, for they are represented only by two surviving species of bats. However, since the sea is no barrier to aquatic mammals, we are compensated by having a considerable fauna of whales and seals.

Whales

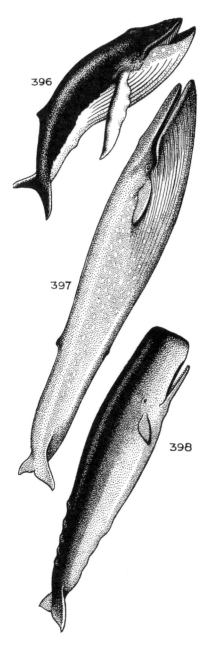

396. **Humpback Whale** (*Paikea*)
Megaptera novaeangliae
This is the most abundant large whale in New Zealand waters. It grows to 16 m long, and is an ungainly creature with large knobby-edged flippers, reaching up to 4 m long. It is a "whalebone" species, that is, the mouth is fitted with long, closely-packed flexible plates, or baleen, which serve to strain small animal life from the seawater. Such whales have deep longitudinal grooves under the throat, which allow for expansion when the whale's mouth is distended with food and water. The Humpback was until 1964 taken commercially in Cook Strait, the whaling station being just within the entrance to Tory Channel. Formerly there was a second station at Whangamumu, near the Bay of Islands. These whales were taken during their northward migration from July to August, and again on the return journey in October and November. For the rest of the year the Humpback frequents the cold waters to the south of New Zealand.

397. **Blue Whale** (*Ngutu Kura*)
Balaenoptera musculus
The largest of all living animals. It grows to 30 m long, may weigh over 120 tonnes, and is dark bluish-grey mottled with white on the underside. This whale ranges all seas, but it is most abundant in the Antarctic. It is a "whalebone" species, and it is truly remarkable that such immense size can be attained on a diet of small shrimp-like animals sifted from the surface waters of the ocean. There have been about 10 recorded strandings of this whale from New Zealand waters, one being the now famous Okarito Whale, the skeleton of which, 26 m long, is held by the Canterbury Museum.

398. **Sperm Whale** (*Parāoa*)
Physeter macrocephalus
This is easily recognised by its huge rectangular head and toothed narrow lower jaw. It grows to 18 m long, and during last century was the most sought after whale, both on account of its rich blubber and also for the fine quality clear spermaceti oil taken from the head. A considerable whaling fleet of large sailing vessels made world-wide cruises in search of this species and northern New Zealand, from even before the earliest days of settlement, was a favourite base. The Sperm Whale yields another very valuable product, ambergris. This is a hardened secretion from the intestines which is caused by the irritating action of embedded beaks from cuttlefish, consumed as food. Ambergris has the consistency of beeswax and will melt with a shining surface if a lighted match is applied to it. This substance was used in the manufacture of high-grade perfumes, but actually it imparts no other virtue than a faint musk-like odour which persists long after the true perfume has disappeared. When fresh, ambergris resembles chocolate that has partially melted in the sun, but matured pieces washed ashore on beaches are hard and dark grey, with a white chalky encrusted outer surface.

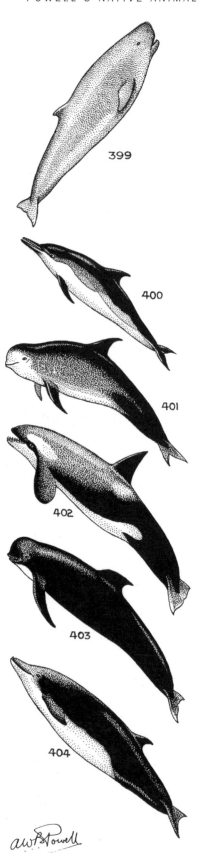

399. *Pigmy Sperm Whale* (Parāoa Teoteo)
Kogia breviceps
This attains a length of 2.5-3.4 m, and apart from its considerably smaller size is distinguished from the true Sperm Whale by the shape of its head, which is less exaggerated, and the form and position of the dorsal fin. Both species have teeth in the lower jaw only. The Pigmy Sperm Whale has a world-wide range, but is never abundant.

400. *Common Dolphin* (Aihe)
Delphinus delphis
This dolphin is often erroneously termed the Porpoise. It is 1.8-2.4 m long and is easily recognised by its well-marked beak and 45 to 50 pairs of small pointed teeth. The Common Dolphin is abundant all round our coasts, and frequently enters harbours. The body is black or dark brown above and white below, with a greyish overlapping area between the two colours. These mammals usually move about in schools and have considerable speed. They are very fond of surfing on the bow wave of moving ships, and their regular broaching of the surface with a graceful, wheel-line motion is fascinating to watch.

401. *Risso's Dolphin* (Pāpāhu)
Grampus griseus
This is best known to New Zealanders by one example, the famous "Pelorus Jack", which for many years attracted wide interest from its regular habit of playing about the bows of steamers in the vicinity of Pelorus Sound. So great was the interest in this friendly mammal that an Order-in-Council was enacted to ensure its protection. The ultimate fate of Pelorus Jack is unknown, but it was last seen in 1912. Risso's Dolphin has a world-wide range, but it is a rather solitary animal, seldom appearing in schools. It grows up to 4m long and is easily recognised by its bulging forehead.

402. *Killer Whale* (Kākahi)
Orcinus orca
The largest of the dolphin family growing to about 9 m. In the summer months they are frequently seen, especially in Cook Strait and the Hauraki Gulf. Killer Whales are found in all seas, feeding mostly on squids and fish, though in Antarctica they also hunt seals and penguins. There are instances of Killer Whales bumping the under surface of ice floes whilst Men were standing on top, and they frequently rear their heads high out of the water to peer across the ice in search of likely seal victims. However, there are no actual records of deliberate or fatal attacks on Humans. This whale is recognised by its robust shape, large rounded flippers, and in adult males a very tall triangular dorsal fin.

403. *Blackfish* (Ūpokohue)
Globicephala melaena
Sometimes called the Pilot Whale, this species grows to 6.5 m long, and is entirely black except for a small area of white under the chin. It has a bulging forehead and a broad-based dorsal fin, flattened on top and curved backwards. These whales move about in huge schools, and not infrequently get stranded on beaches and perish. A whale's body is easily supported in water but out of this element the great weight of flesh causes suffocation.

404. *Goose-beak Whale* (Mōmori)
Ziphius cavirostris
This occurs occasionally in New Zealand waters. It attains a length of 6 m and there is a single pair of conical teeth at the tip of the upcurved beak-like jaws. The colour pattern varies, but is mostly purplish-black above and white below. The species has an immense distribution from Sweden to South Africa, Argentina, India, Australia and New Zealand.

405. Hector's Dolphin *(Tūpoupou)*
Cephalorhynchus hectori

This grows to about 1.6 m long, and is distinguished from the Common Dolphin by its shorter beak and rounded dorsal fin. It is black above and white below with the upper portion of the snout grey. This species is seen in small schools in coastal waters, but does not occur outside the New Zealand area.

Seals

406. New Zealand Sea Lion *(Whakahao)*
Phocarctos hookeri

This grows to 3.5 m long and breeds on the subantarctic Auckland and Campbell Islands. The male is a heavily-built animal with a thick coat of long dark-brown hair. The hair is especially thick and long on the neck and shoulders, and is disposed like a mane. The female is smaller, more sleek, and grey in colour. The coat of this species is not nearly so valuable as that of the Fur Seal, but nevertheless a very considerable sealing industry operated from Sydney in the early nineteenth century. The Auckland Islands were the centre of this activity, since these animals were very abundant there, and that group possesses several fine harbours. Today the world population is only a few thousand. Sea Lions are clumsy on land, but in the sea they swim with great speed and agility. Their food consists largely of fish.

407. New Zealand Fur Seal *(Kēkeno)*
Arctocephalus forsteri

This is much smaller than the Sea Lion, the maximum length being about 2 m. It is distinguished by its pointed nose and reddish chestnut under-fur, with longer sparse hairs. The fur of this animal is the most prized of that of all seals, and for this reason the species has been subjected to most ruthless killing. In 1824 one expedition took about 75,000 skins from the south of New Zealand, and during the peak of the sealing trade no less than 400,000 skins were taken from the Antipodes Islands alone. These seals dwindled to such an alarming extent that the New Zealand Government gave them legal protection. They breed on the subantarctic islands, on the south-west coast of the South Island, on Stewart Island and on the Chathams. Elsewhere on the mainland there are numerous non-breeding colonies occupied mainly in winter.

408. Leopard Seal *(Popoiangore)*
Hydrurga leptonyx

This grows to 3.5 m long, and is longer in the body than either the Sea Lion or Fur Seal. Also its hind limbs are fused like a tail and are not capable of being turned forwards, nor can this animal rear the fore parts of its body into an erect position. The hair is short, the coat being greyish, sprinkled with black spots and some white ones on the sides. This species is abundant in Antarctic seas, and is an occasional visitor to the shores of New Zealand.

409. Elephant Seal *(Ihu Koropuku)*
Mirounga leonina

Found in breeding colonies at Macquarie and Campbell Islands and other subantartic groups. It is a huge mammal up to 5.5 m long. In colour it is uniformly brown. The proboscis of the male, which is greatly distended when the animal is disturbed or angry, is a most distinctive feature. Elephant Seals were formerly killed in numbers for their blubber, but not for their fur.

Bats

Our only native land mammals are three small species of bats, one of which is now extinct and the others rare. The surviving species are known respectively as the Long-tailed Bat and the Short-tailed Bat. Alternatively, they could be referred to as the "Short-eared" and the "Long-eared", for curiously the long-tailed has short ears and the short-tailed has long ears. The Long-tailed Bat occurs in many districts of the main islands of New Zealand and close relatives are found in eastern Australia. The Short-tailed Bat is much rarer and has no close relatives beyond New Zealand.

410. Long-tailed Bat *(Pekapeka Tou Roa)*
Chalinolobus tuberculatus
This bat shelters in caves and in hollow trees. It is greyish-brown and has a span of about 150 mm. These bats have a soft noiseless flight, and finally come to rest suspended head downwards by the claws of their hind limbs. The food is largely flying insects.

411. Short-tailed Bat *(Pekapeka Tou Poto)*
Mystacina tuberculata
Widespread but local in heavy bush of the North Island. Now very rare in the South and Stewart Islands. Bats normally pursue insects on the wing, but the short-tailed species certainly can climb and walk by means of folding the forepart of the wings and using them as legs. It thus eats fruit, nectar and ground insects as well as flying prey.

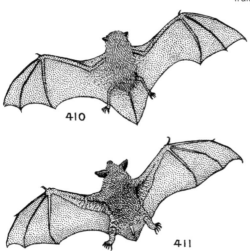

410

411

Further Reading

GENERAL
Morton, J.E. & Miller, M.C. 1968. *The New Zealand Sea Shore*. Collins, London.

MOLLUSCS
Penniket, J.R. & Moon, G.J.H. 1970. *New Zealand Seashells in Colour*. Reed, Wellington.
Powell, A.W.B. 1976. *Shells of New Zealand*. 5th ed. Whitcoulls, Christchurch.
Powell, A.W.B. 1979. *New Zealand Mollusca; Marine, Land and Freshwater Shells*. Collins, Auckland.

ARTHROPODS
Chapman, A. & Lewis, M. 1976. *An Introduction to the Freshwater Crustacea of New Zealand*. Collins, Auckland. (Contains a section on freshwater spiders and mites.)
Forster, R.R. & Forster, L.M. 1973. *New Zealand Spiders. An Introduction.* Collins, Auckland.
Forster, R.R. & Forster, L.M. 1980. *Small Land Animals of New Zealand*. 2nd ed. McIndoe, Dunedin.
Gibbs, G.W. 1980. *New Zealand Butterflies. Identification and Natural History.* Collins, Auckland.
Miller, D. 1984. *Common Insects in New Zealand*. 2nd ed. (revised by A.K. Walker.) Reed, Wellington.
Winterbourn, M.J. & Gregson, K.L.D. 1981. *Guide to the Aquatic Insects of New Zealand*. Bulletin of the Entomological Society of New Zealand No. 5.

FISH
Ayling, A. & Cox, G.J. 1982. *Collins Guide to the Sea Fishes of New Zealand.* Collins, Auckland.
McDowall, R.M. 1978. *New Zealand Freshwater Fishes; a Guide and Natural History.* Heineman, Auckland.
Paulin, C. & Roberts, C. 1992. *The Rockpool Fishes of New Zealand*. Museum of New Zealand, Wellington.
Paulin, C.; Stewart, A.; Roberts, C. & McMillan, P. 1989. *New Zealand Fish. A Complete Guide.* GP Books, Wellington.

AMPHIBIANS & REPTILES
Gill, B.J. & Whitaker, A.H. 1996. *New Zealand Frogs and Reptiles.* David Bateman, Auckland.
Robb, J. 1986. *New Zealand Amphibians and Reptiles in Colour*. 2nd ed. Collins, Auckland.

BIRDS
Heather, B.D. & Robertson, H.A. 1996. *The Field Guide to the Birds of New Zealand.* Viking, Auckland.
Kelly, C.T. 1982. *Collins Handguide to the Birds of New Zealand*. Collins, Auckland.
Robertson, C.J.R. (ed.) 1985. *Reader's Digest Complete Book of New Zealand Birds.* Reader's Digest, Sydney.

MAMMALS
Baker, A.N. 1983. *Whales and Dolphins of New Zealand and Australia: an Identification Guide.* Victoria University Press, Wellington.
Daniel, M. & Baker, A. 1986. *Collins Guide to the Mammals of New Zealand.* Collins, Auckland.
King, C.M. (ed.) 1990. *The Handbook of New Zealand Mammals.* Oxford University Press, Auckland.

Index of Generic Names

Index of Common Names

This index is limited to the most familiar common names and to group names.